Robert Peary

Boy of the North

BY

Electa Clark

ILLUSTRATED BY

Bernard Barton

THE BOBBS-MERRILL COMPANY, INC.

Publishers

INDIANAPOLIS   NEW YORK

To my little girl
JENIFER
the gentlest critic
an author ever had

ACKNOWLEDGMENT

I wish to acknowledge the help given me by Marie Peary Stafford, the explorer's daughter, in providing me with information about her father's cousins. Many of the stories in this volume are based on facts published in the book *Peary*, by William Herbert Hobbs, published by The Macmillan Company in 1936. I also drew upon *Peary: The Man Who Refused to Fail*, by Fitzhugh Green, published in 1926 by G. P. Putnam's Sons.

ELECTA CLARK

CONTENTS

CONTENTS

LIST OF FULL-PAGE ILLUSTRATIONS

ROBERT PEARY

Boy of the North

I

ROBERT EXPLORES

THE LITTLE boy stared up at the distant hill. It was thickly covered with green trees.

"How I wish I could climb that hill!" Robert Peary said to himself. "I wonder how far I could see if I shinnied up the very tallest tree on top of it and looked away off."

Robert looked back over his shoulder at the little house where he lived alone with his mother. He wished she could go walking with him right now—walking on and on toward that wonderful hill. But of course she was too busy cooking.

He walked just a few steps out of the yard and down the road. His eyes were on the faraway hill. When he looked down he saw some butter-and-eggs blooming bright and yellow in a field.

15

He stopped to pick a handful. Then he ran after a bee that flew along heavily. Its legs were golden with pollen. From the woods farther ahead he heard a loud cawing and scolding.

"Maybe the baby crows are out of their nests!" Robert exclaimed. He hurried to see. There they were—rows of small crows with short tails and wide-open mouths. They sat side by side on the branches of trees. He laughed to see the big, black parent birds stuffing food into the open bills. "I've been hungry, but I've never felt anywhere near as hungry as they look," he thought. "Their mouths look bigger than all the rest of them put together."

He walked on. "Now I'm right in the woods," he told himself, "so I may as well go a little farther."

Step by step he wandered farther and farther from home. There was so much to see! He was curious about so many things!

"Oh," he exclaimed suddenly, "there's a baby raccoon!"

He ran forward and picked up the furry creature. Its paws were like thin, black hands. Its pointed nose was black, too. Its bright eyes stared up into Robert's face.

Robert sat down on the ground and cuddled the raccoon like a kitten. "Where's your mother?" he asked. "Why aren't you playing with your brothers?"

Then he sat very quiet to listen. But he heard no sound of a mother raccoon scampering through the Maine woods. "Are you lost?" he asked the small animal. "You look mighty thin and hungry. Shall I take you home and feed you?"

The raccoon was wriggling and whimpering. But it didn't seem a bit frightened at being held.

Robert stood up and looked about. He was on a rocky hillside. Fir trees grew all around him.

He could not remember which way he had come. "Why," he said out loud, "I'm the one that's lost!"

But if the raccoon wasn't afraid, he wasn't going to be. He turned in the direction that he thought should lead him home. He held the raccoon tight in his arms and trudged down the hill. He looked at everything he passed.

Suddenly he stopped. "Now I'm going uphill again!" he said to the raccoon. "This can't be the right way home."

While he stood still, he heard the gurgling of a brook. "I may be lost," he thought, "but I've just got to explore until I find that brook." He pushed his way through bushes and over rocks. In a few minutes he came to the bank of a stream. He stooped down to splash his hand in the cold water.

Then he had an idea. "Maybe this brook goes downhill and runs into the creek. If I follow it, perhaps I'll come to the creek too. Then I'll know where I am, and I can find my way home."

Robert stood up and began to walk beside the brook. The baby raccoon was growing heavy in his arms, but he wouldn't put it down. He stepped along quickly.

He had been right. By and by the brook flowed into the larger creek.

"I can see the church steeple in town from here," he said to the raccoon. "Now we're not lost any more." He went on along the creek bank toward the town of Cape Elizabeth.

Just then he heard a voice calling. "Bert! Robert Peary!" The voice had an anxious tone.

Robert began to run. "Mother!" he shouted. "Here I am, Mother! I've something to show you!"

In a few moments he saw his mother hurrying toward him. Her long black skirts were caught up in one hand to keep them out of the dust.

"Mother!" Robert shouted. "I've something to show you."

"Bert," she exclaimed, "I've been so worried about you!"

He hugged her waist with one arm while he held up the raccoon with the other. "Look!" he said excitedly. "Look at this baby raccoon! I'm going to call it Little Mac, after our brave general McClellan who is fighting for the Union in

Virginia. I'll feed it and look after it. It'll go everywhere with me, won't it, Mother? Just like a pet dog."

Mrs. Peary looked down at the small animal. She stroked its soft, furry back with her fingers. "Raccoons bite," she said in a doubtful tone.

"Not Little Mac," her son said confidently. "This coon's good. It was lost, and I think it's hungry, too. Have we any fish to give it? Will you let me keep it for a pet, Mother?"

"I suppose you may keep it for a while," Mrs. Peary said. "We can't very well just turn it loose to starve, without its mother."

She took Robert's hand in one of her own, and they began to walk toward their house. She looked down at him gravely. "Bert, why did you run away?"

"I didn't run away. I just wanted to look at that hill. So I walked along, and pretty soon I was lost. Then I found Little Mac, and then I found myself."

"But you're only six," his mother scolded gently. "You know you mustn't play outside our yard."

"Yes," Robert agreed. "But, Mother, please climb that high hill with me soon!" He looked back over his shoulder. He looked up the slope longingly. "I wonder what you can see from away up there!"

"I suppose," Mrs. Peary said, "you could see all of Casco Bay. You'd see waves breaking on the shore. You'd see tall rocks in the water, and little islands. And you'd see farms and forests."

Robert sighed. "I wish I could see them now," he said. "When I'm big I'm going to climb all the hills in Maine! Then I'm going to see everything in the world. I'm going to places where nobody ever went before. Oh, Mother, I wish I were big *now!*"

II

THE PET RACCOON

1. *Little Mac in Mischief*

ONE morning in the winter of 1863 when the pet raccoon was nearly a year old, Robert ran downstairs to breakfast. His face was beaming with fun. "Mother," he cried, "someone slept with me last night. Guess who!"

Mrs. Peary was bending over the kitchen fire, turning pancakes on a griddle. She looked up in surprise. "Someone slept with you," she repeated. "What do you mean?"

Robert broke into a laugh. "Little Mac!" he exclaimed. "Last night was cold, and in the middle of the night I woke up and felt it jump into bed with me. It snuggled under the covers and crawled down to my feet. Then it curled up and slept by my feet all night."

23

"Oh, Bert," his mother said, "animals shouldn't sleep in bed with people!"

"But Little Mac's so clean," Robert said. "Its fur is always clean, and its feet too. You know how often it goes swimming."

Little Mac had become a member of the family. It was so tame that it never bit anyone. It was a pretty creature. It had a black stripe across its face like a mask. It was covered with yellowish-gray fur. Its long, thick tail had rings of black. Little Mac had grown steadily fatter, rounder and bigger all the time.

"Well, yes, your pet is a neat little animal," Mrs. Peary agreed. Then she began to laugh. "Look at it now!" she exclaimed. She pointed to the kitchen shelves.

There was the raccoon on the top shelf. It was standing on its hind feet and using its front paws like hands. It was lifting the top from a small crock of honey. As it worked, its bright

"Quick, Little Mac!" cried Robert.

eyes were fixed on Mrs. Peary's face. The raccoon knew that she would chase it away from the jar of honey if she saw it.

That was just what Mrs. Peary did. She seized a broom and waved it. Little Mac scrambled down from the shelves in a hurry.

Robert ran to open the kitchen door. "Quick, Little Mac!" he cried.

The raccoon sped outdoors before Mrs. Peary could spank it with the broom.

Robert often brought home fish for his pet. He fed it bread and butter, corn and apples. He kept a pan of water in the shed so that the raccoon could wash its food before eating. Best of all food, it loved sweet things, like preserves.

"Bert," Mrs. Peary said one day, "have you been taking maple sugar from this drawer without asking me if you might?"

"Why, no, Mother," Robert said. "But now you mention it, I'd love to have some."

"Well, I thought I left a big chunk of maple sugar here. But there isn't any now."

2. *What Happened to the Maple Sugar*

A few days after that, Robert's Uncle Eben Nutter came to see them from Fryeburg. He drove up to the house in his two-horse sleigh.

The Maine roads were too icy for wagon wheels.

Robert ran out to greet him. "Uncle Eben, Uncle Eben!" he cried. "Will you take me for a ride?"

He was always glad to see Uncle Eben. He danced around the sleigh and patted the big mares. Nelly and Sal's sides were steaming in the cold.

Uncle Eben laughed as he tossed his bearskin robe aside and jumped down to the ground. "Yes, I'll take you for a ride after a while," he said in a deep, firm voice. He draped warm gray blankets over Nelly and Sal to keep them warm. "I came to see if you and your mother will go back to Fryeburg with me for a visit."

Robert was really excited. He loved to see his many young cousins and his grown-up relatives in Fryeburg.

Uncle Eben stamped the snow from his heavy boots and went into the house. Robert followed him. "Here, my boy," he said, "I brought you a bag of cinnamon drops." He hunted through his pockets until he found the red candies.

"Oh, goody!" Robert opened his mouth wide and was about to stuff a handful into it when he caught a glimpse of himself in the little mirror on the wall. "Why, I looked like a baby crow!" He laughed. "May I have some now, Mother?"

"Suppose you eat three now," his mother said, smiling. "Put the rest away to eat after dinner."

Robert ate three of the cinnamon drops slowly. Then he put the rest into a drawer of the kitchen dresser.

When Uncle Eben sat down in the warm kitchen, Little Mac jumped up into his lap. With its little paws it began to go quickly through Uncle Eben's pockets. In a minute it brought out a thick gold watch. The raccoon loved anything shiny.

Uncle Eben roared with laughter. "Why, you

little woods thief!" he cried. "Give me back my watch. Raccoons can't tell time."

Still laughing, he grabbed the watch and tucked it back into his pocket. He pushed the raccoon off his lap.

Robert sat listening to the two grownups talk. "Mother!" he cried suddenly. "Look at Little Mac!"

The raccoon had quietly opened the dresser drawer and was holding the bag of cinnamon drops in its black paws. When it saw everyone turn to look, it quickly took a handful of candies. It thrust them into its mouth as fast as it could. It didn't have time to wash the candy first.

Mrs. Peary jumped up from her chair and seized the broom. That was enough warning for Mr. Raccoon. It dropped the bag of candy, climbed down from the dresser and scampered to the door.

Robert was there ahead of his pet. He held

the door wide. "Run, Little Mac, run!" he
shouted.

Once more the raccoon got off without a
spanking.

Mrs. Peary laughed and put down her broom.
"Now I know what happened to that maple
sugar," she said.

III

ROBERT SHOVELS SNOW

"WE'RE PACKED in as tight as three mackerel in a salt barrel," Robert said with a laugh.

Mrs. Peary had cordially accepted the invitation to visit her relatives in Fryeburg. Robert had been careful to leave plenty of food for his raccoon. He wondered if Little Mac would be there when he got back.

He and his mother and Uncle Eben had set out on the trip the next day. They tucked themselves into the sleigh, with Robert in the middle. He was pressed so close between the two grownups that he couldn't move either way.

The bearskin robe covered him to the chin. His coat collar was turned up. His fur hood protected his ears. His feet rested on a stone which his mother had heated in the fire and then wrapped in a quilt. His face stung from the cold wind, but all the rest of him was warm.

They spent the night at an inn and were off again early next day. Nelly and Sal clip-clopped along the hard, white road beside the Saco River. Steam blew back from their nostrils.

"It's beginning to snow!" Robert exclaimed. "I feel a snowdrop on my nose. It tickles."

A few minutes later Mrs. Peary said, "It's snowing harder and harder. Oh, dear, and we're still a long way from Fryeburg!"

Uncle Eben peered up at the dark-gray sky. "Looks as if there's plenty of snow up there," he said. "Maybe we'll have a blizzard."

"Hurrah!" Robert said. "Then we'll have to stay at Fryeburg for a long time!"

The snow kept falling faster. The drifts were piling up. But Nelly and Sal seemed to know exactly how to get home, even when they had to bend their heads low against the wind. They

They had tucked themselves into the sleigh.

lifted their feet high to get through the thick, dry snow.

They reached the edge of town and stopped when they came to Aunt Martha Nutter's big house.

"Climb down, Bert," Uncle Eben said. They went into the house.

Robert found the big kitchen wonderfully warm and gay after the cold drive. He loved the noise of children's voices and women's greetings after the quiet loneliness of his own little home.

Robert grinned at everyone. Uncle Ben was there too. Pretty Mary Elizabeth ran up and gave him a big hug. A friendly collie dog rubbed against him. His cousin Janette helped him take off his heavy coat and hood.

"Bert, come see my new snowshoes," Cousin Walter called.

"You're going to sleep with Walt and me," announced Cousin Frank.

All the family was talking at once in lively confusion. Bert was glad to see how happy his mother looked among her own kinfolk. At home she was often sad and silent. That was because she missed his father. He had died four years before in Cresson, Pennsylvania, where Robert was born.

Now Mrs. Peary was talking gaily to the other women. She was hurrying to tie a big apron over her dress so that she might help cook supper.

"Men! Boys!" Aunt Martha called. She waved a big cooking spoon. "Just look at that snow outside! Are you going to let us be snowed clear under?"

There was a rush for mufflers, caps and high boots.

"Who's the goat? Who has to shovel the long walk?" Cousin Walt sang out.

There were five separate paths to be cleared. There was the long walk out to the road. There were the short paths to the stable, to the pigpen, and to the well. The shortest path was the one to the chicken house.

"Come on, boys!" shouted Cousin Frank. "Let's draw straws to see who's the goat."

"Where's your broom, Mama?" Cousin Emma asked.

"Right behind the stove, same as always," her mother answered briskly.

Cousin Emma found it and pulled several straws from the broom. She broke four into short lengths and left one long. She held them half hidden in her hand. "Everybody take one," she said.

Walter and Frank, Uncle Eben and Uncle Ben clustered around her. They looked hard at the straws, trying to guess which were the short ones. The one who pulled out the longest straw had to clear that long walk to the road.

Just then Robert cried, "Wait for me! I want

to shovel, too." He was tugging hard to pull his big boots on over his shoes.

"No, no, you're too little. You stay inside and keep warm," Aunt Martha said.

"No, please, I'm not too little," Robert insisted. "I can shovel snow just like a man. Can't I, Mother?"

Mrs. Peary smiled. "You do work almost as well as a man, Bert."

Robert stood in the ring with the cousins and uncles. He reached out a hand for a straw. He tried to guess which would be the long straw. He took one. Everybody whooped. "Bert's the goat! Bert got the long straw!"

"Well, he can't do that long walk," Aunt Martha said. "You shovel the short path to the chicken house, Bert."

"No. If I got the long straw, I must do the long walk," he said and grinned. He went into the storeroom with the other boys and picked out a snow scoop. He tramped with a sturdy tramp, to sound as much like his bigger cousins as he could.

Outside, the snow whipped angrily. It blew in his face. Already it lay quite deep on the ground. He bent and scooped a big shovelful off to one side. Then another. And another. "Hurrah!" he cried. It was fun to toss the heavy loads away. It was fun to feel the icy air on his cheeks.

He looked back to see how far he had come. It was only a few feet. He stood still for a moment and gazed around him. Trees and buildings were shadows against the white of the snow. The fence carried a smooth little hill of snow along its top.

Robert turned back to shovel snow. He swung into the work gladly. But before long his arms grew tired. Then his back began to ache.

How mighty far it was to the road!

39

"Ouch!" he groaned. "I'm the goat all right."
Well, he had drawn the long straw. He wouldn't
stop till he had cleared the long path.

"Bert!" someone called from the house.
"Come on in! Uncle Eben will finish your
walk!"

"Thanks, but I'll do it," Robert called back.
Painfully he picked up one more scoop of snow.
How awfully heavy it seemed now! How mighty
far it was to the road! Another scoop. Another.
Another.

Sweat trickled coldly down his forehead. It
got in his eyes. But he kept on and on. And then,
when he felt he'd just have to give up, he came
to the road. His job was done! He bent over
and lifted one last, heavy shovelful of snow. He
turned and started for the house. He dragged
his scoop behind him.

He found his mother waiting for him at the

kitchen door. "Bert, that was a hard task," she said.

"I made up a rhyme." Francine giggled.

> "My cousin Robert Peary
> Shoveled till he was weary."

"Bert deserves the biggest slice of roast goose!" Cousin Walt said.

"Good for you, boy! Even your Uncle Eben never heaved that much snow when he was only seven," Aunt Martha said.

And Uncle Eben himself boomed out in his deep voice, "You can stick to it, lad."

Robert tugged off his boots and unwound his muffler. He was so tired that he sat down to unfasten his coat buttons. But he smiled at his mother. "I'm all right. Don't worry about me."

She gave him a proud look. "When Robert Edwin Peary starts a thing," she said to the relatives, "he finishes it!"

IV

AFTER THE SNOWSTORM

ROBERT woke up the next morning to see dazzling light pour through the windows. He
jumped out of bed. The floor felt like ice to his
bare feet. He ran to a window and breathed a
hole in the ice that caked it on the inside.

It must have snowed all night, he thought
excitedly. The world outside was all dark green
and shining silver—pine trees and snow. Thick
curls of smoke rose from every house in sight.
Paths around the Nutter house were cleared.
Robert saw that the men of the family had already been busy. "Gosh, I'm glad I don't have
to shovel the path to the road again!"

Now Cousin Walt was stirring in his bed.
Cousin Frank peeked sleepily over the top of the
covers heaped on him.

"Come on, get dressed," Robert urged. "I want to go out of doors."

The other boys groaned. "Not going to get me out of my warm bed," Frank mumbled.

Robert began to pull on his clothes. He shivered in the frosty air of the bedroom. He ran downstairs.

His mother and Aunt Martha were busy in the kitchen. They were setting the long table, and stirring hot pork gravy on the stove.

"Good morning, Mother. Morning, Aunt Martha," Robert said. He kissed his mother. Then he ran to the stove and warmed himself in the fierce heat pouring from it. "Doesn't this feel good!" he said.

"You're up early, bear cub," his aunt said cheerily. She tweaked a lock of his red hair. "Run out to the woodshed, will you, and bring in an armload of wood? Can't keep enough

wood on hand these cold days. The stove just
eats it up!"

Robert laughed. He wrapped himself in coat,
muffler and boots and ran to the woodshed. The
air was so cold it stung his nose and eyes. The
world was too bright to look at with wide-open
eyes. He danced over the snow. He loved the

Robert carried in armfuls of wood.

creaking noise it made under his boots. He made several trips in to the wood box. He carried in armfuls of cut beech logs and birch logs.

"There!" he said, panting. "That'll feed the old stove for a while!"

By now every cousin was downstairs. Just as it had been yesterday, the kitchen was full of hubbub and bustle. The little girls wore long, warm skirts and braided hair. They were putting the steaming breakfast on the table. The boys had on tight-fitting trousers and thick shirts. They loaded the stove and hurried to the henhouse with hot corn for the chickens. Everybody was busy, and everybody talked.

"May we go for a walk in the woods, Aunt Martha?" Robert asked when he could make himself heard above the racket. "I love to be out after a blizzard."

"Land sakes, why don't you stay where it's

cozy?" His aunt laughed. "You children can play all day by the kitchen stove."

"But I want to make tracks in the new snow," Robert said.

"Sure, let's all go out," Cousin Walt said. "We'll take our sled. Maybe we can find a good place to slide."

They sat down to breakfast. Robert ate fried ham and codfish balls and hot biscuits with butter. Afterward the children rushed out into the brisk winter air.

"The snow's so deep it's hard to run in," Robert said. He took two steps, fell flat, and stumbled to his feet, laughing.

The other boys and the girls floundered and fell down, too. But they got up and plowed their way forward again. They laughed, too.

"The snow's too powdery to make good snowballs," Cousin Janette said. But she threw handfuls of loose snow at Cousin Francine.

"Bert's the first to get his face washed!" Walt shouted.

"No, I'm not!" Robert shouted back. "You can't catch me!" He tried to run, but the snow was too deep and he tripped. At once Walt pounced on him. The boys rolled over and over, sputtering and laughing.

"There!" Walt yelled. He rubbed a handful of snow on Robert's face. Robert got to his knees and brushed the snow from his cheeks. In a moment they were tingling.

"I'll get even!" Robert shouted. He ran after his cousins. He couldn't catch them, but he managed to fling a handful of snow down the neck of Frank's coat.

"Ouch! Ouch! I'm freezing!" Frank shrieked as the snow melted against the skin of his back.

The girls had been dragging a sled behind them. "Here's a hill where the wind has blown some of the snow away," Janette called. "It's just right for sledding."

"Me first!" Francine shouted. She flung herself face down on the sled. Girl and sled shot rapidly down the hill, around a tree, and ended— *flufffff!*—in a snowbank. Snow sprayed back over Francine like a wave.

When she stood up, Walt called, "You're as white as a snowman!"

The sled was upside down, buried in snow, but it was not damaged.

"Let Bert and Mary Elizabeth go down next," Janette said when the sled had been dragged uphill again.

"I'll sit in front, Little Un," Robert said. Mary Elizabeth sat behind him on the sled. She clasped her arms around his waist. Both children shrieked with joy as the sled plunged downhill.

Then the other girls and boys took turns sliding. They pulled the sled up and scooted down.

Up again and down again. The wind was so cold that it brought tears to their eyes. Their cheeks burned fiery red.

Finally Robert grew tired of waiting at the top of the hill for his next turn on the sled. He wandered away by himself. He bent over to study a row of dimples in the snow. "A fox ran this way in the night," he decided. "These are his tracks."

Farther along he found a line of tiny footprints. He knew these were made by a little woods mouse. Suddenly he stood stock-still. Ahead of him were three rabbits romping in the snow. They rolled over and over. They kissed noses. Then they saw him. For an instant they stood as if frozen. Then their furry white tails flashed. They dived into a hole in the snow that led to their burrow.

Smiling, Robert walked slowly on. The only sound was the creaking of cold, stiff tree branches moving in the wind. Ice shone on them.

Ahead of him stretched a long, sloping hill. "I'll find out what's beyond it," he decided. He began to run clumsily through the snow. He felt that when he reached the top of the hill he would discover some wonderful thing.

"Bert!" came a distant call from behind him. "Bert Peary, where are you?"

He stopped and looked back. He had walked so far that his cousins were out of sight.

"Yo-ho!" he shouted. He cupped his hands around his mouth to make his shout carry farther. "Yo-hooooooo!"

"We're going home! Come along!"

Robert stood still. He was eager to see what lay over that dazzling white hilltop. "I'll come home la-a-a-ter!" he called at the top of his voice.

But Cousin Walt yelled, "Come now! You have . . . to come . . . with us!"

Robert sighed and began to trudge back toward his cousins. He found his way easily by following his own tracks. As he walked he kicked up shining white fluffs of snow with his toes. But he wasn't thinking about the snow just then. He was thinking, "Someday I won't have to mind what older people tell me. I'll be old myself. I'll decide what to do. I'll be a traveler. I'll go to see all the far-off places I want to."

He rejoined his cousins. They all felt cold by this time, even Robert. "Race you home, Little Un," he shouted.

They ran. They fell down in the snow. They laughed and got up, bumped into each other and fell down again. It was lots of fun.

That evening the children had another kind of fun. They made popcorn balls in the big, warm kitchen. The balls were sticky with molasses and melted butter.

Robert fell asleep full of happiness. Visiting cousins was wonderful!

V

SCHOOL DAYS

1. *Robert Has a Wish*

"Look! There's Little Mac! He's waiting for us," Robert cried.

He and his mother had stayed in Fryeburg for five more days. Then the road was clear enough for them to go back home. Once more they had climbed into the sleigh. Again Uncle Eben drove them.

As they stopped in front of the Pearys' cottage Robert caught sight of his pet near the door.

He scrambled out from under the bearskin robe and jumped to the ground. He lifted the fat little raccoon in his arms. He laughed to see the black paws search among his coat pockets.

"Yes, I brought you some candy," Robert

said. "I have some maple sugar for you. When I get in the house I'll take off my coat and find it."

After Uncle Eben had driven away, Robert and his mother sat talking in front of the warm stove. Little Mac, well fed and warm, lay asleep on Robert's lap. Mrs. Peary sat in her straight chair and darned the worn-out knees of Robert's long black stockings.

"Mother," Robert said slowly, "don't you think the way we live is rather lonesome?"

"You mean that you miss having other children to play with?" Mrs. Peary asked. She dropped the mending in her lap and gazed thoughtfully at her son. "Yes, I can see that this is a lonely life for you. That's partly the reason why I like to take you visiting to Fryeburg."

"But I might go to school," Robert said. "If I went to school, I'd be with other boys every day. My cousins go to school—even the girls."

"But, Bert," his mother protested, "you're learning fast here at home."

"I know," Robert agreed. He was quick to add, "I know you're a good teacher, Mother. I can spell a lot of long words——"

"You've learned to read almost as well as I can. You're learning the multiplication table," Mrs. Peary said.

"I can say my tables right up to nine times nine," Robert said.

"I'm sure you wouldn't have learned any more if you had been going to school."

"Maybe I wouldn't, Mother. But . . . but other boys go to school. Walt and Frank do. I want to be like them, Mother. And like Uncle Eben. Please, Mother."

Mrs. Peary looked sad. She carefully guided her needle in and out of the stocking she was mending. "Well, Bert, if you think you should," she said at last, "I'll see about your entering a city school."

"In Portland, Mother? That'll be wonderful!" Robert bounced with excitement. Little Mac growled a little in his sleep. He didn't like a jiggling lap.

"Portland is about six miles from here," Mrs. Peary said thoughtfully. "You couldn't walk there and back every day."

"I can walk part way," Robert said. "Mr. Williams takes vegetables into the city to sell every day. It's not far to his place over at Pond Cove. I'll ask him if I can ride to Portland with him."

2. *The New Boy*

Three weeks passed. Robert was afraid the spring term might end before his mother enrolled him in school. But at last she said one day,

"I've been talking to the principal of School Number Three in Portland. He says you may enter next week."

"Next week! Hurrah! I'd better study hard on that multiplication table. I almost know up to twelve times twelve now, but I'm a little unsure. I'd hate to look dumb in front of a whole roomful of boys."

He ran to find his shabby old arithmetic book.

The next Monday morning he was up at daybreak for an early breakfast, and then off on his walk north to Pond Cove. Mr. Williams had told Robert he'd be glad to have a passenger to Portland.

In the city Robert stepped shyly into a strange schoolroom. It was a big, dusty room. Because the windows were narrow it was rather dark. At the front was a platform with a desk on it. The teacher sat there. Robert had been told his name was Rounde.

Facing the schoolmaster were about twenty boys. They sat at desks in rows. Pens and copybooks lay on the desks in front of them.

The room was so quiet that the *squeak-squeak* of Robert's new school shoes sounded very loud indeed. One of the boys giggled. Robert felt his ears burn. All the same, he walked straight ahead, across the big room, with his heavy shoes going *squeak-squeak . . . clump-clump*. When he reached the master's desk he said, "Good morning, sir. I'm Robert Peary."

He looked straight into Mr. Rounde's eyes. He held his chin up. His voice came out loud and firm. It sounded as much like Uncle Eben's voice as Robert could make it. He wasn't going to let anyone guess how shaky he felt.

Mr. Rounde was a man of middle size with fierce-looking black whiskers on his cheeks. He looked down sternly at Robert and said, "Good morning. I was expecting you. Sit at that desk on the end. We'll begin our work in five minutes."

Robert looked around and saw that there was a vacant space on the front row. He walked over to it and sat down. He made himself very busy arranging the schoolbooks that he had brought from home. He put them in a neat stack on the desk before him. Then he picked up his goose-quill pen and pretended to study its point very closely.

He knew that all the boys were watching him. He felt Mr. Rounde's stern gaze on him. For a minute he wished he were home in his mother's kitchen.

Then the boy sitting next to him leaned forward and peered up into Robert's face. He had curly dark hair and twinkling eyes. He was grinning. "Hello," he whispered. "Don't let old Rounde scare you. He doesn't bite. He's got a switch, but he's human."

Robert managed to smile.

Just then Mr. Rounde tapped sharply on the desk and stood up. He looked sharply over the rows of boys. "While you older boys study your Latin," he said, "the younger ones will have a lesson in geography."

Geography! This will be fun, Robert thought. He folded his arms on the desk, leaned forward and relaxed a little bit.

Mr. Rounde faced a small blackboard on the wall behind his desk. In a firm hand he drew an outline map of North America. Then in a gruff voice he said, "Point out New York Harbor, John Stanley."

A tall boy walked to the blackboard and took Mr. Rounde's piece of chalk. He made a careful dot at the place on the outline where he thought New York Harbor should be.

"Correct," Mr. Rounde said. "Ned Reynolds."

This was the boy with the curly hair who sat beside Robert. Ned scrambled to his feet and went up to the blackboard.

"Point out the Rocky Mountains," Mr. Rounde said.

Ned made some wiggling lines with the chalk to show where the Western mountains lie. Then he went back to his seat. He caught Robert's eye and grinned. Robert winked at him.

The lesson went on. Robert began to feel excited. Those snaky lines on the blackboard represented real rivers! Those white dots of chalk stood for real cities. He was hearing the names of some of them for the first time today!

He waved his hand in the air. He had seen other boys do this when they wanted to speak.

Mr. Rounde nodded to Robert.

"Sir," Robert said, "all the rivers and towns

and lakes are on the bottom half of the map. What's in the top part? Is that all ocean?"

Mr. Rounde moved his hand slowly across the blank part of the map. "The Great North," he said. "This is the great unknown—the land of ice and snow. Only a few explorers have gone into that frozen country- -not many."

"Oh," Robert said. "Then you can't mark rivers and lakes in the north, because nobody knows what's in that country?"

Mr. Rounde nodded. "Who knows?" he said. "Who knows what may lie up there, hidden in the Arctic!"

The words thrilled Robert. "The Arctic!" he whispered to himself. "Oh, how I'd like to see it!"

But while the new pupil was intent on the geography lesson, some of the other boys grew restless. Spitballs began to fly at the back of the room. A book banged on the floor. When Mr.

Rounde turned his back to the class the big boys scuffled and guffawed.

Mr. Rounde whirled around to face the students. His eyebrows were drawn into a scowl. His black beard looked more fierce than ever. "Fulton!" His voice sounded like a bark. "Beaney! Come here, sirs!"

Two boys walked unwillingly up to the schoolmaster.

Mr. Rounde whipped out a ruler from his pocket and said, "Your hands, please!"

He lashed the ruler hard across the palms held out for him—three sharp blows for each boy. Then the boys returned to their seats. They were grinning and pretending that their hands didn't sting.

In one corner of the room the schoolmaster kept a long, limber birch switch. Whenever the class became unruly he would switch the boys' legs with it.

"You may have a recess," Mr. Rounde announced.

In the middle of the morning Mr. Rounde announced, "You may have a recess."

The boys slammed their books to their desks.

They sprang up from their seats and made a rush for the door. Outside they whooped and ran about like wild Indians.

Robert was the last to leave the schoolroom. He felt shy. He wondered if these rough boys would want him to play with them. They might only tease him, he thought. But outside the door he found curly-haired Ned waiting for him.

"Hello," Ned said.

"Hello," Robert answered. He scuffed one of his newly shined school shoes in the dust.

"How do you like jail?" Ned asked. He jingled some marbles in his pocket.

"You mean school? I like it fine. Don't you?"

Ned made a face at the schoolroom windows. "Naw, I hate it." But his voice didn't sound angry. "Old Rounde isn't so bad a master as some, though. He doesn't whip too hard. And, when the weather's good, sometimes he lets us out early because he likes to go fishing."

The two boys walked aimlessly around the schoolyard.

"What do you like to do best?" Ned asked.

"Oh ... take hikes in the woods, I guess," Robert said. "What's your choice?"

"Fishing in Casco Bay," Ned said. "And hunting. I like to play ball and marbles too. Don't you?"

"Why, I don't know. I never have played ball, or marbles either."

"You haven't!" Ned exclaimed. He stared at Robert in astonishment. "Well, do you like to run races? Or hurdle fences to see who can jump the highest?"

Robert grinned. "I don't know," he said frankly. "Those are all things you do in crowds. I've never had a chance to try them."

Ned's face showed his amazement. "Well!" he exclaimed. "You are the funniest boy!"

By this time Ned and Robert were standing at

the edge of the schoolyard. Robert was watching a game that a group of boys were playing. "That looks like fun," he said. "What are the rules?"

Ned said, "See—the boys standing in a ring are the Outsiders. One of them hurls the ball and tries to hit a boy inside the circle. The Insiders try not to get hit. When an Insider gets the ball, he throws it at an Outsider. Every hit is a score. If you catch the ball it doesn't count."

"The ball looks hard. Does it hurt when it hits you?"

Ned said, "It can be a pretty rough game sometimes."

"I'd like to play it," Robert said.

"All right, let's," Ned said carelessly. He stepped up to the ring of Outsiders. He pushed his way between two of them and almost at once caught the ball. He threw it quickly at one of the prancing, dodging boys inside the circle. He whooped with joy when the ball landed squarely on the boy's shoulder.

It was easy enough for Ned to join the game. All the players were his friends. For Robert it was different. The boys were strange to him, and the game was strange. No one on the playground could have guessed that it took real courage for the new boy to join the ring of Outsiders.

The other boys looked at him doubtfully. Should they let him play? Or should they trounce him, to find out how much of a licking he could take before he cried? Robert looked straight back at the boys on his team. His face was calm. He wasn't smiling. He looked as though he would fight right back if he had to fight.

Then one of the Insiders cried out in a shrill voice, "Catch the ball, Peary!"

Robert turned quickly and caught the ball that was hurled at him. He threw it at an Insider. The Insider muffed it. It went between his legs.

An Outsider across the circle picked it up and threw it again. The boys shouted and hopped up and down with excitement.

Robert was hit once. The ball stung him for a moment. But he picked it up, took careful aim and got in a clean hit. He shouted whenever his team scored a hit. He groaned whenever the other side made a score. His teammates quickly forgot that he was a new boy. He was one of them.

When the game was at its most exciting pitch, Mr. Rounde appeared at the door of the schoolhouse. In his hand was a big bell. He clanged it hard.

"Recess is over," someone groaned. From all over the schoolyard, boys began to walk slowly back to the classroom.

Ned ran and threw an arm around Robert's shoulders. "You did all right," he said. "I never saw anybody learn a game faster."

"It was fun," Robert said. He liked Ned Reynolds. He knew already that they were going to be friends. He liked playing with his schoolmates, too. And even though he was naturally shy, he knew now that he was brave enough to face up to them, either in the classroom or out on the playground.

VI

A GAME OF SHINNY

1. *Failure*

ROBERT got ahead in school. In a few weeks he was at the head of his class. Then Mr. Rounde moved him to the higher class—a group of boys older than he. But Robert was tall for his age, as well as smart. So he felt at home among boys of nine or ten.

He played every day at recess. When spring came the boys played marbles. Robert quickly became expert.

A much harder game to learn was shinny. Each player found for himself a good, strong stick. Then the boys chose up sides. When the game began, both teams met in the middle of the playground. Between them was a stone about the size of a small ball. The object was to send the stone spinning down the playing field and make it hit the goal. One goal was a dead tree at the end of the playground. The other goal was a hollow stump at the opposite end.

It was a fast, tough game. The stone couldn't be kicked or thrown. It had to be hit with a shinny stick.

When the leader said "Go!"—how the shinny sticks flashed! How the stone bounced over the ground—now toward this goal, now toward that! Players bumped together. Boys were knocked down. The stone would crack against a shin. Flying sticks and swinging elbows struck accidental blows on heads, on arms, on faces.

Robert had never seen this game played. When the first game of the season was about to start, someone said, "Want to play, Peary?" He answered good-naturedly, "Oh, I suppose so."

He was handed a strong stick and put on Ned's team. Robert said, "Show me how to play, will you, Ned?"

"Oh, there's nothing to it. You just try to hit that stone, and shoot it down toward the dead tree. It's easy."

But it wasn't easy for Robert. When he tried to hit the stone, he couldn't. If he stood still and took careful aim, the boys on the other team swooped down and hit it before he swung. If he hurried and made a fast swipe, he missed. Then the end of his stick would only send up a spray of dirt from the ground.

Robert was hit in the knee with a shinny stick. His feet were trampled on. Someone's head struck him in the mouth. He grew dizzy.

At last he landed a hard blow and sent the stone flying down the field. But he had sent it the wrong way! The stone landed smack on the stump. All he'd done was score a point for the wrong team. How the other side laughed and jeered! They called him "Wrong-Way Peary."

Robert was glad when the clang of Mr.

Robert landed a hard blow.

Rounde's bell announced the end of recess. He walked with Ned Reynolds toward the school building. "What a game!" he said, panting.

"Nobody can be good at everything," Ned said in a consoling tone. "You stick to marbles and never mind shinny."

Robert frowned. "No," he said resolutely. "I'm certainly no good at shinny now, but I can learn!"

Ned looked up. He was surprised at the fiery tone of Robert's voice.

After school Robert hitched a ride with another farmer who lived near Pond Cove. When he got home that evening he carried his shinny stick with him. He said "Good evening" to his mother and laid his books on the kitchen table. Then he walked out of the house and through a wood lot to a field near by. He was sure he would be alone there.

He found a stone of the right size. He took

the shinny stick firmly in both hands and hit the stone a fierce blow. It rose in the air and sailed for about fifteen feet. Robert trotted over to it. He hit it back to where it had come from. Then he hit it again. Back and forth. Sometimes he missed his blow, but more often he didn't. He practiced dodging. He pretended that he had an enemy team to play against. He practiced aiming the stone at a target.

Time passed and the light faded to twilight. Still Robert swung his stick, and ran, and swung again.

At last he heard his mother calling, "Bert! Robert Peary! Come in for supper."

Only then did he discover how tired he was. His legs ached from so much running. The palms of his hands were sore from gripping the rough stick.

He let his stick drag behind him as he plodded toward the house. "I need more practice," he muttered to himself. "I'm not good enough. But I *can* learn shinny. I'll show 'em!"

2. *Success*

The next day was Saturday, when there was no school. This gave Robert another chance to practice.

On Monday, when all the boys tumbled out of the school building for recess, Robert shouted, "Who wants to play shinny?"

"Let's play something else," Ned Reynolds suggested. "Shinny isn't your game."

But Robert only raised his voice again and shouted, "Come on—choose your sides!"

Ned shrugged and said, "Oh, all right. I'll be on your team. But if you get hurt, don't forget I warned you."

Boys swarmed over the playground. They found shinny sticks they liked and lined up in the middle of the field.

"The old stump is their goal," Robert shouted. "Let's hit it. Are you ready? *Go!*"

At his shout, all the boys hurled themselves forward. Sticks flew. Elbows swung. Heads bumped as everyone tried to take a swing at the stone. But Robert ducked lower than anyone else. He gave the stone a blow that sent it skimming over the ground toward the stump. The group of boys raced after it.

Robert ran after it too, but he circled around the group. He saw that Ned was in the thick of the crowd. "Ned!" he yelled. "Shoot it my way!"

Above all the noise, Ned heard him. He managed to push the stone out of the crowd. It came bouncing toward Robert. He jumped toward it and swung his stick with all his might. He sent the stone flying through the air. It landed with a sharp *crack* on the stump!

"Hurray for our side!" someone shouted.

Boys threw their sticks into the air to celebrate the first score of the game. Someone clapped Robert's shoulder.

Then the two teams quickly formed in lines again, and the game went on. It was so exciting that everyone was surprised when Mr. Rounde's bell announced that recess was over.

All the boys flocked toward the schoolhouse. "Say, Bert," Tom Jeans exclaimed, "you're a whiz at shinny! Let's play on the same team again tomorrow, shall we?"

"Sure," Robert answered.

Ned asked him curiously, "How did you do it, Bert? Last Friday you could hardly ever hit the rock. And today you never missed it."

"I practiced," Robert said. "I just tried and tried. I'm glad you think I do better. Shinny is a grand game."

VII

ROBERT TO THE RESCUE

1. *Six Rocks in a Row*

BY THE time Robert was ten, he and his mother had moved to a small house in Portland. Robert liked living near his school. He was glad he didn't have to take that long trip twice a day. Even more, he liked living near Ned Reynolds. The two boys enjoyed doing everything together.

One Saturday in the spring they decided to go fishing.

"Where shall we go this time?" Ned asked. "Shall we fish in the bay? Or would you rather find a good pool in the woods?"

"We've already fished all the pools," Robert said. "Let's try some new place today."

Ned laughed at his friend. "You're always hunting for some new place," he teased. "What's wrong with the old fishing places, anyway? The one where we went last Saturday was stuffed with fish."

"Nothing's wrong with the old places," Robert said cheerfully. "Finding a new place is more fun—that's all. Listen, Ned, do you remember the string of rocks that runs out into the bay? Six big rocks in a row, about two miles north of town?"

"You mean the ones we looked at through my father's spyglass one day?"

"Yes. Let's go there and try it. I bet we can catch a lot of fish up there."

"Well, that's a long way to go just to catch fish," Ned said. "But I don't mind."

The two boys hiked along the road that led out of town. They tramped past fields that were ready for spring planting. Then they were in the pine woods, and at last on the shore of Casco Bay itself.

"There's our chain of rocks," Robert said. He pointed. "Let's try to get out to the farthest big one."

"Why, Bert, you can't step from one rock to the next one!" Ned exclaimed. "They're too far apart. You'd have to swim, and the water's too cold for that."

Robert only laughed. "What if they are far apart?" he said. "We can take off our shoes and roll up our pants and wade. Come on. Don't be a sissy."

Robert was already sitting on the sand and unlacing his shoes. Barefoot, he leaped onto the first of the rocks that led out from shore. He balanced on one foot and waved his fishing pole in his hand. He pretended that he was about to fall into the water.

He jumped to the second rock. Then he leaped nimbly to the third. The step to the fourth rock was a little harder, but he landed safely. "Come

"Come on out," Robert called.

on out," he called. "Here's where we start to wade. There's a longer stretch of water between me and the next rock."

"I'm coming," Ned answered. "I'm not a squirrel like you, but I'm coming."

Six feet of water separated Robert from the next in his chain of rocks. He thought he could see a narrow ledge connecting the two rocks

"Here's where we start to wade."

under water. He put in one foot. The water was icy cold, but he did not draw back. The second step on his little bridge took him deeper. At the third step the water was nearly up to his knees. He edged along step by step. At last, one giant-sized jump took him out of the water and right onto the firm, dry rock beyond.

"Hurray!" he shouted. "I'm getting there."

He leaped to the next rock. "Here's a kind of steppingstone that leads to the last one," he called to Ned. "Only it has sloping sides, so it's easy to slip on. Watch out for it."

He balanced carefully on the steppingstone. Then he jumped to the last of the big rocks.

"Here's where we'll fish," he announced. "This is as far out to sea as we can go. The rocks beyond here aren't big enough for us both to sit on."

While Ned teetered and clambered out to the big rock, Robert sat down and baited his hook.

2. *The Storm*

"I suppose these rocks are clear under water at high tide," Ned said. Like Robert, he too was getting his hook ready.

"Yes, and they're under water when there's a

storm," Robert added. "But it's a fine place for fishing, isn't it?"

Ned looked about him. "Why, there's a storm coming up right now," he said. "We've been so busy climbing out here we just didn't notice."

Robert glanced up at the sky. "I did," he said. "I've been watching it move our way. But maybe it'll just give us a drenching and won't be so bad that we'll have to go home."

"A drenching!" Ned exclaimed. "Who wants to be out in a cold rain this time of year? The fish won't bite, anyway, during a storm."

"Oh, well," Robert argued, "we came here to fish. So let's try to catch something, storm or no storm."

The two boys sat on the big rock and tried to coax fish to take their bait.

Twenty minutes passed. The wind blew stronger and stronger. Back on shore the tall pine trees began to whip back and forth. Dark clouds swept low over the water. The color of the bay changed from cheerful blue to a dull and angry gray. Choppy little waves hit at the chain of rocks. The boys drew their bare feet higher to keep them dry.

The first drops to fall were large, smacking ones. Then the rain came down faster. It fell in small, sharp needles. Thunder growled and lightning snapped. In a very few minutes the boys were soaked to the skin. Ned shivered.

Robert swept wet hair out of his eyes and stood up. "I guess you were right, Ned," he said with regret. "We won't catch anything today. Do you want to go back home?"

"Do I!" Ned exclaimed. "Right now!"

The boys wound up their fish lines and put the poles over their shoulders.

"Follow me," Robert said.

He jumped to the steppingstone, then onto the

big rock beyond it. Next he had to wade across the narrow ledge that joined two boulders.

"Tide's coming in. The water's deeper now than it was awhile ago," he called over his shoulder to Ned. "Maybe you were right about swimming after all."

But he was laughing as he stepped carefully along. He felt his way with his bare toes. The water was now above his knees. As it swept back and forth between the two rocks its motion almost upset him. But Robert balanced his body as lightly as a cat and did not lose his footing. In a moment he climbed onto the broad, smooth surface of the next in the chain of rocks.

He turned to look back at Ned. "When you get this far," he called encouragingly, "the rest is easy."

Ned laughed. "Easy for eels. But just watch *me*. I'll probably take a header to the bottom of the bay!"

"No, you won't," Robert said. "Just take care when you—— Watch your step! Steady now!"

Ned had stepped carefully into the gray water. He felt his way along the slippery bridge—one step, two steps, three steps. But then an unexpected wave came up and smacked him behind the knees. The blow threw him off balance. His left foot slipped from the ledge. He yelled. He waved his arms wildly. Then he half turned and flung himself toward the rock where Bert stood. His fishing rod flew from his hand and landed in the water. It began to dance, little by little, toward the open sea.

Robert dropped his rod. "Here, Ned! Catch my hand!" he cried. He reached for the other boy.

Ned was a good swimmer. He was used to playing among the rocks of the bay. But as he fell his head struck a rock. He was stunned. Instead of reaching for Robert's hand or scrambling to his feet, he rolled helplessly into the water.

3. *The Rescue*

"Ned!" Robert exclaimed in alarm. There was no answer.

He kicked off his trousers. Feet first, he slid into the cold water. Almost at once his toes touched Ned's limp body. Diving under, he groped with both hands. Just as he dived, Ned rolled off the rocky ledge where his clothing had caught. With his eyes wide open under water, Robert looked about him. He felt here, there, with both hands as far as he could reach.

But he could not see or feel Ned.

In a few seconds he had to come up for air. His glance swept quickly over the surface of the bay. Ned had not come up.

Robert breathed in as much air as his lungs could hold. Then he dived again. This time he went deeper, headfirst among the rocks. He could see very little through the dark water. He was growing frightened that his friend might drown.

He never paused in his search. He let the air out of his lungs little by little. He knew he couldn't hold his breath much longer.

Then his groping fingers touched something. Was it seaweed? No, it felt like a shirt. It *was* a shirt! Robert twisted the cloth firmly in his right hand to get a good grip. Then he threw one arm around Ned's waist.

He pushed hard against the nearest rock with both feet. Up, up, up went both boys. Their heads and shoulders shot out of the water. How wonderful to feel air against the skin! Robert drew deep breaths with his mouth open. They were safe!

But Ned's head rolled limply on his neck. Robert looked anxiously at him. Ned wasn't all right, after all. He wouldn't be all right till he got him ashore.

Robert looked toward the beach. It seemed a mile away. It had been a quick trip when they hopped over the rocks. It was a long way to carry another boy.

"I could never lift him from one rock to the next," Robert said to himself. "He's too heavy. His clothes are waterlogged. I've got to swim."

The waves rolling toward shore were growing bigger. Sharp rocks lay between him and the beach. There were not only the ones jutting out of the water which Robert could see. There were the more dangerous ones below the surface that he couldn't see.

He braced himself against one of the boulders in the chain of rocks. He wrapped his arm firmly about Ned's chest. He held his head so it would be above water. He faced toward the shore.

Robert held Ned's head above water.

He waited until the next wave was nearly abreast of him. Then he pushed strongly against the rock with both feet. He paddled hard with his left arm and kicked both legs.

Helped by the rolling wave, he swam halfway to shore without stopping. Then he looked at Ned. It was getting harder to keep his face above water. Robert tried to lift him higher but could not manage it.

Robert's right leg scraped against a hidden rock and he felt a stinging pain. He lowered his feet carefully. Hurray! They hit bottom. He could walk the rest of the way.

He carried Ned to the beach.

The last few steps were the hardest. Ned's limp body seemed heavier out of water than in it. But Robert held him by the shoulders and pulled him at last out of reach of the water.

"Maybe he has swallowed too much water," Robert thought anxiously. He was panting. His leg hurt.

He remembered what Mr. Rounde had told the school about saving a drowning person. He turned Ned over and laid him face down on the beach. He paused to get strength.

Suddenly Ned began to stir. Hurrah! Maybe he hadn't swallowed so much water after all. Ned choked and coughed. He opened his eyes and looked about, dazed. He tried to speak. "Where am I?" he whispered.

Robert sat down wearily beside Ned, with his head between his knees. The rain was not coming down so hard now. The wind was letting up. The cut along his shin was clean, not deep. Strength began to pour back into Robert's strong young body. Grinning, he told Ned, "You said we'd have to swim if we fished from those rocks. Right you were! I swam. You had a free ride. Take it easy, fellow. You hit your head on a rock."

Robert saw a lobsterman's cabin a little way down the beach. "Think you can make it to that hut?" he asked.

"Yes . . . if you'll help me," Ned stammered. "I feel a little dizzy and my head hurts."

Robert got Ned to his feet. Ned threw an arm over Robert's shoulder. Together they staggered toward the cabin. The lobsterman saw them from a window and came running out to meet them. He assisted them into his warm hut.

He was a man of few words, but he knew just what to do. He made the boys strip and wrap themselves in blankets. He pulled up chairs for them close to his hot stove. He fixed some broth for them. He put a neat bandage on Robert's leg. He hung up their clothes to dry. He lent Robert a pair of trousers. When they'd had a good rest he went to fetch a neighbor who owned a wagon. He laughed off their attempts to thank him.

So Robert and Ned were driven home in comfort and arrived little the worse for their adventure. On the way Ned said repeatedly, "You saved my life, Bert!"

Robert said, "You'd have done it for me. Say no more about it. But, gosh, Ned, aren't these Maine lobstermen great people?"

VIII

ADVENTURE IN THE TREETOP

1. *The Hawk's Nest*

THE next Saturday afternoon Robert finished his chores as fast as he could. Then he ran to Ned Reynolds' house. "Ned!" he shouted. "Where are you, Ned?"

Ned strolled out of his father's stable. He had a spade slung over his shoulder. "Where are you going?"

"Looking for nests," Robert called. "Do you want to come?"

"Sure thing. I've seen some good nests. I didn't have a basket with me so I didn't take them. Let's collect nests and start a museum."

"No," Robert said firmly. "The birds built those nests this spring. They need them for their families."

"I suppose that's right," Ned said slowly. "It wouldn't be fair. We could look for them, though."

"That's what I'd planned to do. I've been writing down a description of every nest I see." Robert pulled a notebook from his shirt pocket. "I write them in here."

"There wouldn't be any harm in keeping deserted nests, would there?" Ned asked.

"No—not if we're certain they're deserted."

"Sounds all right to me," Ned agreed. "I'll get a notebook too. And a basket in case we find empty nests. Just wait till I put away my tools."

Soon the two boys were hurrying down the road that led out of town. They tramped past fields and then made their way into the woods.

"How many nests have you seen this week?" Robert asked.

"Three," Ned answered. "A wagtail war-

bler's, a bobolink's and a yellow-throat's. They
were easy to find."

"I know—they all nest near the ground."

"How many have you seen?" Ned asked.

"Two I've never seen before," Robert answered. "A screech owl's and a barred owl's."

"Those nests must have been mighty hard to
reach!" Ned said. "How did you get to them?"

"One was at the top of a cliff," Robert said.
"At first I wasn't sure I could climb it, but I finally figured it out."

"It sounds as if you like to look at the nests that
are hard to get to," Ned remarked.

"Sure," Robert said with a grin. "The harder
they are to find, the more fun it is."

Now the boys were out of the low hills and
climbing steeper ones. They were among dark
pines and spruce and cedar trees that grew close
together. The smell of the trees mingled with
the smell of the sea.

All the while the boys looked about them for birds. They peered up into trees for nests. They listened for bird calls.

"Look!" Robert whispered suddenly. He caught Ned's arm and both boys were as still as statues. They saw a bluish-gray bird about a foot and a half long. It made a sudden swoop from a low branch of a tree ten feet away from them. It darted into a thicket. "That's a Cooper's hawk!"

"It's after that rabbit," Ned whispered. "I saw a little cottontail dive into the bushes."

The boys watched the thicket. Soon the hawk flew out of the bushes again. It swept up to the tree branch, folded its wings and hunched along the branch. Its sharp eyes peered at the ground.

"The rabbit got away," Robert said. "It must have its hole under those bushes."

"The hawk's not going to give up," Ned mur-

mured. "It's going to wait right there for the rabbit to come out."

"Look up there!" Robert said. "See that nest in the tree beside the one the hawk's in? Maybe that's its nest."

Ned squinted. "Sure enough—in the top branches. I guess you wish you could climb that tree."

Robert walked all around the tree. He looked up, studying the branches overhead. "Maybe I could," he said thoughtfully.

"Oh, go on!" Ned scoffed. "Some of the branches at the top grow so far apart that you couldn't reach from one to another. I don't think you could make it to the top if you tried."

"I've been up trees that were pretty hard to climb." Robert grinned. "I'm going to try this one."

"Bert, you're crazy," Ned said good-naturedly. "Come along. We'll find some trees we can climb."

"Not till I try this one," Robert said. "Give me a hand, will you?"

"All right," Ned said. "I won't say another word." He clasped his hands together. Robert put one foot into the cup of Ned's hands. Then by stretching his arms as high as he could he was just able to grasp the lowest branch. He began to scramble up.

2. *The Long Climb*

At first he could pull himself up from one branch to the next. The branches grew almost straight out from the trunk of the tree. Some of them, just as Ned had said, grew very far apart. When Robert reached one he shinnied up the tree like a monkey to the next one.

Halfway up he paused to get his breath. He

looked down and waved to Ned, who was staring up at him. "What's the hawk doing?" he yelled at Ned.

"It won't bother you!" Ned shouted. "It's still watching for that rabbit."

Robert began to climb again. Above him the pine trunk stretched into the sky as tall and straight as a ship's mast. "Ouch!" he exclaimed when a branch tore a hole in his shirt. His hands were covered with scratches and he could feel some on his face.

Finally the hawk's nest was a few feet above him. Robert stopped climbing for a minute. The branches were almost too small to hold his weight. He swayed dizzily as the tree moved in the wind. He shut his eyes tight and gripped the slender trunk hard with his arms and legs.

"I hope Ned wasn't right," he said to himself. "I hope this isn't as far as I can go after all."

He opened his eyes, tipped back his head and

looked up. The hawk's nest was only a few feet above him. Only three—no, four—branches were between it and him. "I've come all this way. I can't go down now after I've got this close."

He pulled himself up to the next branch. He had to move very carefully and slowly so he wouldn't break the thin branches.

Finally he pulled himself up to the last branch. It was short but fairly sturdy. He stood up straight with one arm around the tree trunk. His face was level with the nest.

The nest was big, untidy—and empty! "It's a good thing there's no mother hawk here." Robert was relieved. "She'd be mighty surprised to see me. Hawks don't like people and I'm sure they wouldn't like me to come calling on them."

He looked at the nest carefully. He wanted to remember exactly how it looked so he could write it down in his notebook. He poked the nest gently to see how the twigs were stuck together. "It's messy," he mumbled. "Sticks poked in every which way. But it's strong. It must be to stay together in this wind."

Then he looked all about him. "It's like standing on top of the world!" he shouted down to Ned. "I can see Casco Bay! I can see the waves on the beach!"

"Come on down!" Ned yelled. "You've been up there long enough!"

"Oh, no, I haven't!" Robert shouted and yelled. He leaned back and forth to make the tree sway in the air. He waved his cap above his head and sang "Yankee Doodle" at the top of his voice.

Then he sang, "Yankee Doodle went up north, riding on a pine tree!"

Suddenly Robert calmed down. "Ned will really think I'm crazy." He saw three boys running toward the tree. He began to climb down.

Robert began to climb down.

"Hey, Ned!" a voice shouted. "Why are you standing under a tree and singing?"

Ned grinned at them. "Not guilty, Dave," he said. "I haven't sung a note."

"We heard somebody hollering 'Yankee Doodle,'" Dave Worth insisted. "Hey, ouch!" A pine cone hit him on the head. "Quit that, Tom."

"What are you talking about!" Tom Jeans cried. "I didn't throw that cone!"

Another pine cone bounced off Tom's head. This time the boys looked up.

"It's Bert Peary!" Dave shouted.

"Come down out of that tree! Do you think you're a squirrel?" whooped the third boy, Jim Hunter.

The boys stood silently watching Robert scramble down from the tree. He dropped to the ground from the lowest branch.

"Did you find a nest up there?" Tom asked.

"I saw a Cooper's hawk nest," Robert replied.

"Why didn't you bring it down?" Tom and Dave asked together.

"It was all I could do to bring myself down." Robert laughed. "Look at me—I'm all scratches and tears."

"You had that climb for nothing!" Jim exclaimed.

"It was worth it." Robert grinned. "You'd think so too if you'd been up there. I could see for miles around—farther than I've ever seen before."

"You've got plenty of nerve." Jim stared up at the treetop. "That tree must be fifty feet tall. I doubt if any boy ever climbed it before."

Tom poked Jim in the ribs. "Do you want to have a go at it? We'll wait right here for you."

"No, sir. Let's hunt for some shorter trees. Peary, lead the way. We'll do our best to keep up with you."

Robert pulled the notebook from his shirt pocket. "Just as soon as I write down how that nest was built. Then I'll show you a dandy duck hawk's nest. It's in the top of a spruce tree not far from here."

IX

ROBERT LEADS AN EXPEDITION

1. *A Day of Freedom*

IT WAS A sunny day in March 1867. Robert Peary ran along the rough and hilly road. The air was blowing cold and fresh off Casco Bay. The trees tossed overhead in the wind. The bay was a beautiful blue. Robert could begin to see it now through the trees. Saturdays are wonderful, he thought, and so is springtime. It was great to be nearly eleven years old and about to spend a whole day out of doors!

"There she is!" Robert said eagerly to himself. His eyes were on the trim little rowboat, almost new, that a neighbor had told him he might borrow.

In a few minutes he was sitting in it. With one of the oars he pushed it away from land. He fitted the oars into their locks and pulled strongly on them. The little boat moved smoothly ahead.

As he rowed, Robert watched the gulls. They swooped low over the bay, their sharp eyes on the water. They were hunting for fish that might swim near the surface. Many fishermen's boats bobbed up and down on the waves.

"Bert! Bert Peary!" came a faint call. The words floated thinly on the air, as if from a long distance. Bert stopped rowing. He looked all around him—at the fishermen's boats, at the small islands he was headed toward, at the shore line.

"Here we are! Look this way!" came the voices again. Then Robert waved an arm in greeting. Ned Reynolds and two of their friends were calling him from shore. They were barefoot, and their trousers were rolled up above their knees.

"Come on in!" they shouted. "We're digging clams!"

Robert moved his oars in the water. He looked thoughtful. "Shall I row away?" he asked himself. "That's what I planned—to spend the whole day alone on my secret island. Or shall I go back and play with the boys?"

He wanted to do both things. He liked being alone, and he enjoyed his friends too. He looked toward Eagle Island, the distant spot to which he had been rowing. Then he made up his mind. He turned his skiff and rowed rapidly toward the boys.

"Hello, skipper!" shouted Tom Jeans when Robert was near the shore.

"Come help us dig clams," Tom's younger brother Ezra piped in his high voice.

"Is that your own boat?" Ned asked. He splashed into the shallow water and rocked the boat from side to side, as if he might tip Robert into the bay.

"No, I've borrowed it for today," Robert said. He pretended to aim an oar toward Ned's head. "Stop rocking the boat and listen. I've got an idea that sounds like more fun than digging clams. Let's go camping."

"Oh, boy!" Ned exclaimed. "I love to camp! And Pa will let me go because my chores are finished."

Tom and his brother looked at each other. "Think we can?" Ezra asked eagerly. "Reckon Ma will think we've dug enough clams?"

"Where do you want to camp?" Tom asked.

Robert answered promptly. "On Eagle Island. I've been there. Nobody lives on it or uses it. There's a spring on it for drinking water, and plenty of trees to give us firewood. I know a dandy place to cook and sleep, too. We can play

Indians in the woods, or pirates, or we can go hunting——"

"Come on, boys!" Ned shouted. "Let's get ready!" He began rolling down his trousers, then he ran to find his shoes.

"Wait!" Robert called. The other boys turned to listen. They knew he was their leader on this expedition.

"Let's make a plan," Robert said. "We don't want to row clear out to Eagle Island and then discover we'd forgotten something we needed. Now, each of us can bring a couple of blankets to sleep in. Bring a knife, and a gun, too, if you have one, and some ammunition. We'll try to shoot wild ducks for breakfast."

The boys nodded.

"Ned, doesn't your father have some darts you can borrow?"

"Why, yes, Bert."

"Well, you bring the darts and we'll catch flounder for our supper. I'll fetch a spider to fry the fish in. Tom, do you think your mother would let you have a chunk of pork fat for frying?"

"Sure, we have plenty of pork fat."

"All right, you bring a big chunk, and I'll ask my mother for apples. She'll let me have all that's left from our winter's supply. And anybody that has cold biscuits left over from breakfast, or bread, or potatoes—bring them. Bring whatever food your mothers will let you have."

"How soon do we start?" Ezra asked.

Robert considered. "Let's meet right here in an hour sharp. Don't be late. Anybody that's late gets left."

Robert was grinning as he gave this final warning. He dragged his boat onto the shore, and then all four boys ran up the steep path.

They were whooping with joy. They scattered, each one racing toward his own house.

2. *The Secret Island*

All the boys arrived promptly at the meeting place. They stowed their gear in Robert's boat. He counted all the things over to make sure they had everything they needed.

"Get aboard," he ordered. "I'll shove off, and then Ned and I will row."

As the skiff moved out from shore, Robert kept looking over his shoulder while he rowed. "I'll keep the course set toward Eagle Island," he said.

Casco Bay was dotted with islands. Some were so small that they were only bare rocks thrust up out of the water. Some were so big that there were farms on them. Some had wild forests. The

"Is that Eagle Island?"

boys knew many of the islands by name and had
visited them.

"Is that Eagle Island?" asked Tom, pointing.
"I never heard of it."

Robert laughed. "That's because I named it
myself. So far as you can tell, nobody but me has
ever been on it. So I pretend I discovered it, like
an explorer."

asked Tom, pointing.

It was a long pull out to the lonely spot that Robert had named Eagle Island. There were no other islands within half a mile of it.

"Nice and lonesome, isn't it?" Robert said with satisfaction as the skiff floated toward a mooring.

Little Ezra looked doubtfully at Robert and then at the island. It was thickly covered with pine and juniper trees. "It's lonesome, all right," he agreed. "I'm glad to have company in a place like this. But you're funny. You like to be alone."

"Yes, I think lonesome places are exciting," Robert agreed cheerfully. "Come ashore now. Everybody bring a load of stuff. I want to show you where we'll make our camp."

The three boys followed him. He led the way up a steep bank and through the woods. Soon he came to a clearing. "Here we are!" he announced.

He put down the stack of blankets that he had carried. The other three boys placed their loads on the ground and looked about.

They were standing on a ledge of rock that hung over the water. It was as big as a room and nearly flat. It was protected on three sides. Back of it was the forest, and two fingers of land curved out into the water on its two sides.

"Golly, what a place to camp!" Tom exclaimed. "I never saw a better one, Bert. Here on the rock there's no risk of setting fire to the woods. It's not too windy, either."

"Let's have dinner right now," Ezra said. "I'm hungry. No, I'm starving!"

"We're going to have fish," Robert reminded him. "Ezra, you and Tom go out in the skiff to catch flounder. Ned and I will build the fire. We'll be ready to cook when you come back with the fish."

Suddenly Ned clapped one hand to his head. "Matches!" he exclaimed. "We forgot to bring matches! It'll take us hours to get a fire started."

Robert shook his head. "I brought some," he said. From his pocket he pulled a small bottle. Six sulphur matches were inside it, and the bottle was carefully corked, to keep the matches safe and dry.

"What a brain! You think of everything, fellow," Ned said admiringly.

"I'm captain," Robert said, grinning. "The captain's supposed to do a bit of thinking."

Tom and his young brother had run down to the skiff. They floated out from shore with long darts in their hands, on the watch for flounder they might spear and take to camp for dinner.

An hour later, four boys sat contentedly around their campfire. They were full of fried fish and cold biscuits and apples. Robert tucked some big potatoes into the embers, to cook slowly in the dying fire. The potatoes would be done in time for their next meal.

Later the boys explored the island. Robert knew every square foot of it. They divided into pairs and played Indian. All too soon the day was over. Darkness began to fall. Tired out, but happy, they straggled back to camp.

3. *A Roaring Campfire*

Ezra looked around uneasily. He was nine, two years younger than the others. He looked at the black forest behind him. He listened to the waves breaking on the shore under the rocky ledge. He looked longingly at the faint lights flickering far away, on the mainland. "I want to go home," he said in a childish voice. "You can sleep a lot warmer in bed than on a rock."

"But you don't want to row home in the dark!" his brother Tom protested.

"We came here to spend the night!" Ned exclaimed. "We've had only half the fun we came for."

"I want to go home," Ezra said stubbornly. "It's easy to row in the dark. You guide yourself by one of those lights over there. The lights," he added in a homesick voice, "show where people and houses are."

Robert had been listening thoughtfully. He didn't want to give up a project he had started if he could help it. But he couldn't be unkind to a scared kid.

He spoke now in his captain's voice. "We'll spend the night here. What we need is a fire—a roaring fire. Boys, get out your knives and cut branches off those juniper trees. The wind's off shore, so there's no risk of its spreading to the woods."

He put the homesick Ezra to work, and that was just what Ezra needed. The boys threw armfuls of juniper branches onto the embers of their campfire. The fire began to leap and snap and roar.

"Look at those flames!" Ned marveled. "Look at them jump!"

"It sounds like a Fourth-of-July show," Ezra agreed. The fire was so cheerful that he had forgotten his fears of the dark.

"I'm scorching my face," Tom said, laughing.

The boys stepped back to the farthest edge of the rock to get away from the intense heat. They munched hot roasted potatoes. Robert had remembered to take them out of the fire before they built it so big. Soon they were all yawning. Their eyes blinked with sleepiness.

Robert said, "Let's all go to bed. We want to get up early and shoot wild ducks for breakfast. But first, let me show you a trick my Uncle Eben taught me."

He picked up a long branch and began poking at the fire. It was beginning to die down by this time. He pushed the embers toward the edge of the rock. The other boys found long branches too. Together they raked the fire off the rock. The hot branches sizzled as they fell into the bay below.

"Ouch! This rock's too hot to walk on!" Tom

exclaimed. He danced first on one foot and then the other.

"It'll cool off pretty soon," Ned said. "What's this trick, Bert?"

"As soon as the rock's cool enough to stand on," Robert said, "we'll spread out our blankets where the fire's been. And then we'll sleep as snug as crickets on a stove. It's an old Indian custom."

While they waited for the rock to cool, the boys prowled into the woods to find spring water. All were thirsty. When they came back they decided that their campsite was cool enough.

They spread half of their covers on the rock. Then they curled up together and tucked the other blankets over and around them. Sure enough, the heat from the rock was enough to keep them warm all night.

For a while the boys talked and wiggled. But soon Ned, Tom and Ezra fell fast asleep. Only

Robert lay awake. He was too excited by the out-of-doors to sleep just yet. He watched clouds scudding across the stars. He stared at the tree-tops balanced against the sky.

"Camping out is more fun than anything," he said to himself. "I can pretend I'm lost. I can pretend I'm miles from the nearest living person —some place where no one has ever been be-fore."

Then suddenly he sat straight up. He tipped his head back and stared at the pale sky. A flock of wild geese, dim and black in the night, floated across the sky. They flew in a grand "V" with the leader at its point. Wild, free and distant came the sound of their honking.

"Wild geese!" Robert whispered in delight. "Aren't they beautiful! They're flying away up north for the summer."

In a few moments the treetops hid the flock from sight. Fainter, fainter and fainter their honking drifted back to the boy on the rock. Then they could be heard no more.

Robert snuggled down and pulled the blanket up to his chin. As he sank into sleep he was thinking, "Someday I'll go north, too. Someday I'll find out for myself what those wild geese see up there. Someday . . ."

X

BOARDING SCHOOL

1. *Robert Makes Up His Mind*

AT THE end of the next school year, Mr. Rounde, the schoolmaster, went to the Peary house to talk to Robert's mother. "Mrs. Peary," he said in his blunt way, "I came to advise you to remove Robert from School Number Three."

"Remove him!" Mrs. Peary exclaimed. "But he's doing so well at school! Is there some trouble . . . ?"

"The trouble is that he's taken all the schoolwork we can offer him. And yet he's too young to go to high school."

"Yes, he's only twelve. But his studies——"

"Robert is one of the best students I've ever had in my classes," Mr. Rounde said warmly. "His compositions are especially good."

"I know. I always read them before he turns them in," Mrs. Peary said. She tried not to look proud.

"He's one of our quickest students at mathematics, too."

Mrs. Peary nodded, and she smiled with pleasure.

"But I want to advise you to place Robert in another school—one where he can go on with more advanced work before he enters the high school."

"Another school?"

"Yes, ma'am. Now there are a number of schools that he might enter. But I have been talking about him to a friend of mine, a Mr. Perkins. He runs a fine boarding school for boys at Gorham."

"Oh—that's only ten miles from here!"

"Yes. Mr. Perkins would give Robert the kind

of work he needs for a year. Then he'll be ready for high school. You think it over, ma'am."

Mrs. Peary talked it over with Robert.

"But Ned Reynolds won't be at Gorham," he protested. "I'd miss him almost as much as I'd miss you, Mother."

"I will miss you, too, Bert. But——"

"And I wouldn't be able to go boating on Casco Bay!" Robert said in a tone of dismay.

"Aren't your studies more important than boating?" his mother asked.

Robert paid no attention to this question. "At boarding school I couldn't tramp in the woods whenever I want to," he went on.

"Well," Mrs. Peary said, "I leave you to decide which matters more to you—hiking and boating, or getting ahead with schoolwork."

Robert sighed heavily. He spent several days thinking it over. At last one afternoon he said to his mother, "I really don't want to go to boarding school. It won't be a bit of fun. But I think I ought to go."

2. *Good-by to Home*

In a few weeks it was time for the fall term to begin. Robert put on his good suit, walked out of the house and climbed into a wagon. In the back of the wagon lay his little round-topped trunk. It was strapped shut, and inside were all his schoolbooks, his clothes, his rock collection and his leaf collection. He had learned a good deal from these collections and couldn't bear to leave them behind.

"Good-by, son," Mrs. Peary said. "Write to me every week. Be good and study hard."

"I will, Mother," Robert said firmly. "I don't want to go away to school. But since I'm going, I'll do my best to make good grades."

Then the wagon rattled away. Mrs. Peary

"Good-by, son," Mrs. Peary said.

waved and waved until the wagon was out of sight. Robert turned around on the high seat, and he waved too. When he could no longer see his mother, he looked sadly down the road ahead of him. He felt so unhappy that he didn't say a word during the ten-mile trip to the town of Gorham.

3. *A "New Boy" Again*

"Well, here we are," said the driver at last. He pulled up his horse in front of a big, rambling frame building.

"Is this the school?" Robert asked in a small voice.

At that moment the front door swung open and a group of boys swarmed out. Two or three were older than Robert, and some were younger.

"Are you Peary?" they shouted. "We've been expecting you. Come on. We're all going to play ball in the field!"

In spite of his sadness Robert couldn't help smiling a little. This was a pleasant way to be greeted. And although he didn't know any of these boys' names, it was nice that they already knew his.

The driver of the wagon began to carry Robert's trunk into the house. The "new boy" climbed down to the ground.

"I suppose I'd better say hello to the schoolmaster," Robert said to the boys. "Then I'll join you."

"No, we'll wait for you," one of them answered. They were staring at him with friendly curiosity.

A thin, bald man with deep creases in his cheeks stepped out of the house. "Ah, this is young Peary!" he said.

He looked keenly at the new pupil. He saw a tall boy with reddish curly hair and a serious face. He shook hands. "I'm John Perkins, the master here," he said. "And these are your schoolmates. There are eight boys this year, besides yourself. This is the head boy, Paul Pound."

Robert thought that Paul looked like a "head boy." He was taller than the others, and fine-looking. Robert admired him at once. He smiled rather shyly, and Paul's answering smile was quick and friendly.

Mr. Perkins introduced the other boys to Robert. "When you have changed your clothes and got acquainted with the boys," the school-master said, "have someone bring you down to my office. Then we'll have a talk about your work."

"I'll take you up to your room," Paul said. "Stand aside, you kids."

The other boys all moved aside to let Mr. Perkins, Paul and the new boy walk first into the house. Although they were noisy and lively, it was plain to Robert that they were also used to doing whatever their handsome and good-natured leader told them to do.

"This is your place," Paul said. He ushered Robert into a very small room on the second floor. In it were a plain table, one chair and a narrow bed. There were hooks on the wall for hanging up clothes. And Robert's trunk already stood in one corner.

Most of the boys crowded into the room with Robert. A redheaded youngster bounced up and down on his cot. Another ran to unstrap and unbuckle his trunk.

"Where have you been to school before? How old are you? Do you like to play ball? Do you have any brothers?" All the boys talked at once.

Robert grinned at them and answered their questions. They certainly were a friendly lot, he decided.

"Come on, you kids," Paul ordered in his

easy, masterful way. "Clear out of here now. Give Peary some room so he can unpack his things."

The other boys slowly began to straggle out of the room. Paul dropped down on Robert's cot for a talk while the new boy unpacked his trunk.

Robert said to himself, "I'm going to like this place after all. And maybe I'll have as much fun with Paul as I did with Ned Reynolds."

4. *The Quarrel*

Robert quickly grew used to life in the boarding school. It was something like living in a big, noisy family—a family of nine boys and a father. It was very different from the home life that he was used to—one boy and a mother.

Mr. Perkins was not very strict. He seldom punished anyone. He let the boys have lots of time for play. He let the head boy, Paul, see that most of the rules were followed.

There was a big iron tub in one of the back rooms of the building. When a boy wanted a bath, buckets of hot water were carried from the kitchen stove and poured into the tub. A schedule of the time allotted to each boy for his bath was posted on the door.

When it was his turn Robert strolled into the bathroom. His towel was slung over his shoulder, and he carried his soap in his hand. He was surprised to find two boys in the room. "Hello, Phil. Hello, Johnny," he said.

Johnny was the smallest boy in the school. He was pouring a bucket of water into the empty tub. Phil, the redhead, poured in a second bucket.

Robert smiled. "You don't have to fill the tub for me," he said. "I'll do it myself." He put his towel and soap by the tub.

"Oh, Phil and I do all the water carrying," Johnny explained. "We're the youngest. We fill the tub and empty it for everyone. We scrub it out too."

"You do!" Robert exclaimed in surprise. "Why, you're too little to carry all those heavy buckets!"

"That's the rule," Johnny said. "Paul always has Phil and me do it."

"Why, it isn't fair!" Robert said in a loud voice. "Why shouldn't every boy carry water for himself?"

Just at that moment Paul strolled into the room. "I heard the racket. What's the matter? You sound angry about something," he said.

Robert turned to him, frowning. "Paul, Johnny says you make him and Phil carry all the water."

"Sure. The youngest kids have to wait on the rest of us," Paul said carelessly. "They polish

"It just isn't fair!" Robert said hotly.

the shoes and fetch the mail and sharpen the pens and shovel the snow. Why?"

"It just isn't fair!" Robert said hotly. "If that's the rule, it's got to be changed."

Paul's friendly smile suddenly disappeared.

He shot Robert an angry look. "I make the rules," he said flatly.

"If they're unjust, I won't follow them," Robert said.

He and Paul faced each other, scowling. Then Robert turned to the two small boys. They were staring with wide eyes. "You can go now," he said. "And you aren't to carry any more water— except for yourselves."

Very slowly Johnny and Phil walked backward out of the room. They weren't sure whom they should mind—their old leader, whom they loved, or this angry new boy, who was setting them free from a tiresome job.

When he and Robert were alone Paul said, "Listen to me, Peary. I won't allow you to upset my rules. I'm the head boy, and what I say is to be done *will* be done."

Robert felt no fear of the handsome leader. "If

a thing isn't fair, I won't stand for it," he answered.

The two glared at each other. Both were angry. Each thought that the other was wrong. Paul turned and walked out of the room.

Robert took his bath, and afterward he emptied the big tub himself. But he felt very unhappy. He didn't want Paul Pound to be angry with him.

For weeks after that the two boys didn't speak to each other. Robert saw to it that Johnny and Phil didn't polish anyone's shoes except their own. He insisted that all the boys take turns at bringing in firewood and carrying away the ashes. When the whole school played games out of doors, Robert watched to see that the two smallest boys weren't teased or treated unfairly.

The boys in school took sides in the trouble between Robert and Paul. Little Johnny and Phil were the only ones on Robert's side. Paul was so popular that all the other boys were loyal to him.

"Who does Peary think he is?" one boy said crossly. "Why should I have to carry wood? I did it when I was the youngest one in school. Now I'm old enough to be waited on myself."

Another boy said, "He's just a new boy, and here he is trying to run the school!"

Another said thoughtfully, "But Peary's fair. He wouldn't stand for anything that wasn't fair."

"Well, that's right. I can't help thinking Peary's right. But things were a lot more fun around here before he began to make new rules."

Mr. Perkins realized that his two best students were on bad terms. But no one told him just what the quarrel was about. He believed that boys should be allowed to settle their own differences. So he did not ask any questions.

XI

HAPPIER TIMES

1. *Game Day*

FOR several months Robert was unhappy at boarding school. He studied hard—just as he had promised his mother. And he did the best work he had ever done. But he knew that he was unpopular with his schoolmates.

To himself he said, "I wish I hadn't had to disagree with Paul. It's awful to have everyone against me. But I had to stand up for the younger boys. And I'm not backing down—not even if the rest of the school is against me till I graduate."

In the spring Mr. Perkins' school always had a "game day." At that time all the parents and many friends of the boys came to visit. The boys put their rooms in apple-pie order so that they could stand inspection by the visitors. And they put on an athletic show for their guests.

Contests were planned—tugs of war and ball games and races. The winner of each contest was awarded a blue ribbon.

Robert hadn't written his mother about the trouble he was in. She came to the school with the other visitors. Robert ran to meet her and threw his arms about her. He showed her his room and took her all over the school grounds. He introduced the boys to her.

"And who is that handsome boy over there?" she asked.

"His name is Paul Pound," Robert said. "Paul," he called, "my mother would like to meet you."

Paul gave Mrs. Peary his warmest, friendliest smile. "Mr. Perkins is proud of Bert, Mrs. Peary. He makes the best marks of any of us."

But there was no friendliness in the look he gave Robert.

As they walked on, Mrs. Peary said, "What good manners that boy has! I'm glad he's a friend of yours."

Robert sighed. He wished that Paul and he really were friends.

When it was time for the games, the visitors stood or sat along the edge of the playground. They clapped after each event. All the boys took part in a handicap race. The onlookers laughed over little Johnny's plucky running. They applauded when Paul threw a ball farther than anyone else. They applauded still harder when he won a hurdle race.

Then it was time for the broad jump. This was a contest for the older boys only. The younger boys couldn't hope to do so well as the big ones.

Paul was known to be the school's best jumper. He stood ready at the end of the track. Then he raced at top speed for a few yards, tensed himself and leaped lightly and beautifully through the air. He landed on both feet, then rolled over and looked back to see how far he had jumped.

"Twelve feet!" Mr. Perkins shouted when he measured the distance.

The audience clapped.

"Who's next?" called the schoolmaster. "Jones! Where's Jones?"

"He hurt his ankle in the hurdle race," someone said. "He can't jump."

"Simmons! Simmons next!" Mr. Perkins called.

"I'm no good at jumping, Mr. Perkins," said Simmons.

"All right, Simmons, we'll let you off. Peary!"

Robert got up from the ground where he had been resting. "I've never been able to jump so far as Paul," he thought. "And I'd hate to show myself a failure in front of all these people. But

Robert hurled himself through the air.

I can't be a poor sport. I can at least try."

He walked back to the starting position. He measured the distance ahead of him. "This *has* to be the best jump I ever made," he said to himself.

He raced forward and hurled himself through the air. He landed with a thump on the sand. As he got to his feet the audience was silent. Then everyone broke into a cheer.

"He did it!" . . . "He jumped a foot farther than Paul!" . . . "Good for Peary!" the schoolboys shouted.

Robert felt surprised. Slowly a grin spread over his face. His schoolmates thumped him on the back.

"Bully for you, Bert!"

"That was as nice a jump as I ever saw!"

Robert found it pleasant to be praised by the boys, but he was puzzled by their friendliness. It was nice to see his mother smile when Mr. Perkins pinned a blue ribbon to his shirt.

A few minutes later Robert saw Paul Pound walking toward him. To his surprise, there was a wide and friendly smile on Paul's face.

"Bert," he said, "that was a good jump, a

whale of a good jump. You made me look like small potatoes. Look here, why can't we be friends? I know I've been wrong about hazing the younger boys. But you made me so mad I wouldn't admit you were right."

"Well, I'd like to be friends, too," Robert said.

"Then let's forget all about it," Paul said. "Come along. It's time to go in and clean up for supper."

He flung an arm around Robert's shoulders and the two boys went toward the schoolhouse together.

2. *"Hard To Stop"*

Now that he was happy at school, Robert studied harder than ever. He enjoyed all his subjects—mathematics, English, history, geography and Latin.

One evening he sat alone in his small room.

"I shall find a way, or make one!"

He was translating the next day's Latin lesson.
He was almost finished, but a few words still
stumped him.

He muttered them aloud twice before he flipped the pages of his Latin book to look them up. Suddenly the meaning of the sentence came clear to him: "I shall find a way, or make one!"

He whispered it over to himself. "Now that's a motto for a man to live by!" he thought excitedly. "That's a motto for a man who wants to reach his goal! Why, a man who has made up his mind to find a way to something—or *make* a way to it—why, he'd be hard to stop."

He put his Latin book away. Then he seized a copybook that lay on his table. A few weeks earlier he had begun to keep a diary. In it he wrote down what seemed important to him among the things that had happened at school. Now he opened his diary to a fresh page. He took up his pen and wrote his new motto in large, firm letters:

I shall find a way, or make one.

XII

A FALL THROUGH THE ICE

BY THE next year Robert was ready for high school. He could live at home again.

One bitterly cold afternoon in winter he went ice skating after school with Ned Reynolds and another high-school friend, John Stevens.

"Let's have a race!" John shouted. He was already swooping rapidly up and down the ice, far from shore.

Ned Reynolds was just stepping onto the ice. "It's mighty thin here at the edge."

Sure enough, a dark rim of water showed at the edge of the ice, right at the shore line.

"It's solid enough farther out," John called. "Come on. Race with me."

But Robert laughed and said, "You two race if you want to. I'm going to practice figure eights."

He skated gracefully in curves. His weight swung now to the left, now to the right. He was a good skater, yet he was not satisfied with his "eights." Over and over he practiced the figure tirelessly. His face stung with cold, but he hardly noticed it.

Twice the blade of his skate caught in a deep crack and he was hurled to the ice. Each time he got up quickly to his feet.

John swooped up close and good-naturedly made fun of him. "You'll never learn to do good eights, Peary," he shouted. "Give up, give up!"

Robert laughed and shouted back, "I *am* awfully slow at it. Looks like it might take me a hundred years, but I'll find the way."

John glided off. "You probably will," he called back over his shoulder. "Knowing Bert Peary, I'd say you will! But you haven't got a hundred years now. It's about time to go home."

Robert began to wriggle toward

Robert glanced at the sun and realized that they had skated as long as they should. "Meet you at the shore," he called. On the still, cold air his voice rang out loud and clear.

shore as fast as he could.

John and Ned skated to the spot on shore where they had left their schoolbooks. At the edge they stepped cautiously. They could feel the thin ice dipping under their weight. They sat down on a rock to unfasten their skates.

John suddenly glanced up to see Robert skating toward shore. He was coming in at a point several yards away.

John sprang up with a shout. "Stop! The ice is breaking!"

It cracked under Robert's weight. It split. One jagged sheet of ice surged up on its side like a broken plate. Down into the black, icy water Robert fell. He sank to his waist.

John and Ned began to run toward their friend.

"Stay away!" Robert shouted. "Keep off the ice near me or we'll all be in the water!"

He scrambled up to the solid ice behind him. Then at full length he began to wriggle toward shore as fast as he could. John and Ned crawled out to help him. The ice was so thin here that they didn't dare to try to walk upright.

Land was only a few yards ahead of him. He

was gasping with cold when he reached the shore.

"Wow! I'll have to run like a deer to keep from feezing to death!" he said through chattering teeth.

Ned and John helped him take off his skates. He stamped his feet. His wet legs ached. "Let's go! Run!" he cried.

The three boys started for the Peary house. They had a mile and a half to go.

"Are you . . . all right?" Ned called.

Robert made a face at him. "Fine!" he said. "Feel just . . . like an . . . iceberg."

In a few minutes water stopped streaming from his trousers. They froze solid except at the knees where his running kept them loose. His frozen shoes wouldn't bend an inch on the hard roads, and his frozen pants legs scraped stiffly against each other. The best he could manage now was a slow trot. The other boys slackened pace to stay with him.

"I sound . . . like a lot of . . . icy branches rubbing on a window," Robert panted.

Through a window Mrs. Peary saw the three boys coming toward the house. She opened the door. "Hello, son!" she greeted. "Hello, boys! Why . . . why, Robert! What happened to you!"

"I fell through the ice," Robert gasped. "John, will you bring some blankets down from my bed?"

John dropped skates and books and went clattering up the stairs. He came running down again with his arms full of quilts and blankets from Robert's bed.

Robert was on a chair beside the hot stove. He was struggling to untie frozen shoelaces with stiff fingers. "Ned," he said, "will you take that tub down off the wall? Then fill it with hot water from the kettle on the stove? A hot foot bath will feel mighty good."

While Robert undressed and wrapped himself

"I feel like an Indian," Robert remarked.

in blankets, Ned filled the tub with boiling water. When the water was cooled just enough, Robert plunged his feet into it. Mrs. Peary made a pot

of steaming tea. She brought out a platter of
ginger cookies. Then she and the three boys sat
around the stove and talked.

"I feel like an Indian," Robert remarked as he
sipped his tea, "all wrapped up in blankets like
this."

Ned said, "Remember the lobsterman's cabin,
Bert? Then it was I who needed this treatment.
I've gone out to his lobster pots with him several
times. He hardly ever says a word, but we have
a grand time together."

"By the way, Bert," John said, "why do you
keep all that junk in your room?"

"Junk!" his friend repeated. "There's no junk
in my room. Are you calling my collections
junk, John?" He pretended to be offended but
he had to grin. He knew how crowded his little
bedroom was. "Mother says my room's so full
an ant couldn't crawl through it. But all I have
is my rock collection and my——"

Mrs. Peary interrupted. "Bert's room is enough to break the heart of a good housekeeper. But he does more than just bring in clutter. He really studies his rocks. He looks them up in books. He knows what each one is and its scientific name."

Ned looked at his friend with admiration. "I know it," he said. "Bert always has to find out about things."

John got to his feet. "Thank you for the tea and cookies, ma'am. I'd better hurry home before my mother wonders if I've fallen through the ice."

John picked up his skates and his books. "Bert," he said, "I've something here you'll enjoy reading." He handed Robert a book. "Give me credit for lugging it around all afternoon."

Robert stretched out one hand from his blankets and took the book. "*Arctic Explorations,* by

Elisha Kane," he said, reading the words on the cover. "What is it—an adventure story?"

"Oh, better than a story! It's all true. This man Kane made an expedition into Greenland a few years ago. He was trying to rescue a party of explorers who had got lost somewhere on the great ice field."

"Thanks. I'll be glad to read it," Robert said.

Ned and John said good-by and left the Peary house.

Cozily wrapped up in front of the stove, Robert opened the book. He read and read. He became so interested that he didn't notice when the room grew dark. He didn't notice when his mother lighted a lamp and set it near his shoulder.

In imagination he was traveling over the glacier. He was in the middle of a vast plain of ice. He was wrapped in furs, cold, footsore and hungry. He was huddled over a small campfire

with a band of bearded companions. He seemed
to hear the voices of his fellow explorers.

"Bert! Robert Peary! Do you hear me, son?
I've called you four times!"

"What? What is it, Mother?"

"It's time for supper. What on earth can be
so absorbing that you can't even hear my voice?"

Robert shut his book reluctantly and laid it on
the table. His eyes were glowing. "Oh, Mother,"
he exclaimed, "that's a great book John lent me!
Elisha Kane must be a wonderful man. He
traveled for days over the icecap, hunting a party
of explorers who had disappeared. He got to
know Eskimos. He camped on ice floes. He
drove teams of Eskimo dogs. Think of it,
Mother! He explored a land that only a few
white men have even *seen!*"

Robert was lost in a dream of the Great North.
He didn't taste the food that he put into his
mouth. He didn't see the warm little kitchen or

his mother's face. He was seeing great ice wastes and polar seas and fur-clad Eskimos.

"Here, let me read part of this to you," he said. He opened the book eagerly and began to read aloud. The last of his meal grew cold on his plate. Mrs. Peary was almost as much interested as Robert was.

At last he closed *Arctic Explorations* again and leaned back in his chair. "Someday," he said yearningly, "someday I've got to see that country in the Far North!"

XIII

NORTHWARD!

ONE AUTUMN day in 1885 a tall young man with a serious face stepped into a second-hand bookstore in Washington, D. C.

"How do you do, Mr. Bolt," he said.

The bookseller bustled forward past tables piled high with books. "I'm sure I should know you, sir. Your face is familiar. But my memory is getting bad. Remind me, please."

"I couldn't expect you to remember me. I came here several times nine years ago when I was in Washington on a college vacation. Nine years are a long time."

"Of course, Mr. Peary. I recall now. Didn't Congressman Horn bring you in? I seem to remember he said you were another Maine man. Weren't you interested in books about the Arctic?"

165

"That's right. I got some good ones from you."

"And your college was Bowdoin, wasn't it?"

"Right again. I was graduated the next year. Then I went into the Navy."

"Like all State-of-Maine men I dreamed of the Navy myself when I was a youngster. But I couldn't make it. How do you like being a sailor?"

"Oh, I'm not a sailor exactly, Mr. Bolt. I'm a civil engineer in the Navy."

"Ah! And where have they kept you at your engineering?"

"I've been far away—in Nicaragua. I was surveying the swamps and jungles down there. The government thinks of building a canal across Nicaragua."

"Well, well! Surveying, now!" said Mr. Bolt, beaming.

"Yes, I've been busy. I've helped design the

"Browse around," Mr. Bolt said.

dams and locks for the canal. Now my work is nearly finished. I have time on my hands."

Mr. Bolt chuckled. "Nicaragua is a long way from Maine. And it's a far longer way from the Arctic. Did it make you forget your old interest?"

"It did not. But down there I couldn't get hold of any books."

"Well, I've picked up some things about the North lately. Browse around. Make yourself at home. It's good to see you again."

Robert picked up a book, leafed through it and put it down. He glanced at the titles of half a dozen other books. Then he chanced on a small pamphlet. Its tattered cover showed that it had passed through several hands. *Greenland,* he saw, was part of its title. He carried it to a spot near the front of the dusty old store. There a hanging lamp made a pool of brighter light.

"The Inland Ice of Greenland!" he exclaimed.

He felt a tingle of delight. "Somebody who has been in the Arctic wrote this pamphlet!"

He remembered the day he had discovered the thrill of Arctic exploration, when he read the book John Stevens had lent him. The marvel of that day swept over him again. It was as if he had read Elisha Kane's book only a week ago.

He thrust his hand into his pocket and brought out a quarter. "Here, Mr. Bolt," he said to the bookseller. "I've found the most exciting reading in your shop!"

He hurried to his rooming house to spend hours reading and rereading the pamphlet. At last he turned off his lamp and stretched out on his bed. But he was wide awake and excited. He was thinking, "No one knows much about Greenland. No white man has ever crossed to the east coast of that frozen country. But I believe it can be done. And I want to be the man who does it!"

He began making plans for a trip to Greenland. He persuaded the Navy Department to give him a leave of absence. His mother lent him five hundred dollars for his expedition.

In May 1886 he set sail on the *Eagle,* a whaling boat, and started on his first exploration to the Far North.

He did not reach the east coast of Greenland —not on that journey. But he learned many valuable secrets of Arctic travel. And he learned one great truth about himself: exploring the Arctic was his lifework!

Peary traveled as a private citizen, not a Navy man. He used all his pay and savings, but still he needed support from friends and members of scientific organizations.

Five years later Robert Peary had enough money for supplies and equipment and again he tried to cross Greenland. With his brave wife and six men he left the ship at the northwestern corner of Greenland in July 1891. They built a cabin and began exploring the land close around them.

Heavy snow was falling the day the first group of Eskimos arrived at the camp. They examined Peary's wooden cabin carefully and then began building igloos. They worked rapidly but all the while they kept talking among themselves and watching Peary and his party.

"What are they saying?" Josephine Peary asked. "I suppose they think their round houses built with blocks of ice are better than our cabin."

"I'm sure they think so," Peary told his wife. "And they don't think this expedition has a chance. One of them said so as soon as he got here."

"That's silly," Mrs. Peary said. "They wouldn't have come here to work with you if they thought that."

"They're curious about us, for one thing. And another reason they came is to sell us dogs."

"I know you can get across," Mrs. Peary said firmly. "The Eskimos will find out soon enough they're wrong."

Peary laughed. "Do you call six months 'soon'? I won't be able to go inland until February at least. The blizzards are getting worse every day. I could never get through storms like these."

In February Peary made his way to the east. He took with him two of his best men—Dr. Cook, the party's doctor, and Eivind Astrup, a young champion skier from Norway.

They plodded steadily along for several days. When they made camp they took off their outer clothes and crawled into their sleeping bags.

One night Peary said, "The wind has changed. The snow will beat down on us harder than before. We'll stop here and use these snow walls one of our scouting parties built."

The men took special care in building a square house of ice blocks. It had just enough room inside for them to lie down in their sleeping bags. They left their clothes and supplies outside the bags. Shivering, they took off their clothes quickly and stretched out in their bags.

As they dozed, the driving wind battered the ice walls and piled up drifts. Suddenly Peary woke up and felt snow whipping against his face. "Dr. Cook! Astrup!" he shouted. "Wake up! The wind's wearing away the walls."

The doctor sat up and looked around him. He was almost covered with snow. He groaned. "Why did we leave our fur clothes outside the bags!" He shook the sleeping Astrup by the shoulder.

The men rolled free of the drifts over them and huddled together with their backs to the wind. They dozed from time to time as they waited for the storm to die.

After many hours Peary woke up in darkness to hear a rattling sound against his hood. He stuck his hand out through his sleeping bag. "Rain!" he exclaimed. "It's freezing as it strikes!"

He moved a little in his bag. It was already stiffening as it began to freeze. "Cook! Astrup!" he shouted against the roar of the wind. "Roll in your bags every few minutes. If you don't you'll be frozen solid to the ice."

The rain lasted only about an hour but then snow began swirling again. The men slept fitfully as the hours passed. Toward morning the storm died away.

"We have one thing left on top of the snow," Peary said. "I've kept this shovel by my hand. We'll have to dig down deep into these drifts for the rest of our things."

Peary tried to dig out their supplies. He moved awkwardly. He was still bundled up in his bag, and he was stiff from lying so long in the cold. After a while he managed to uncover a fur jacket, a pair of trousers and a pair of seal-skin boots. "Here, Astrup. Put these on and take a turn at digging."

Astrup wriggled out of his bag. He dressed quickly and started to dig. "Here are Dr. Cook's clothes," he announced finally. "And here are yours right under them, Lieutenant Peary."

"Anything's better than lying any longer tied up in a sack," the doctor said with a grin. "Now I can get some exercise."

Peary shook himself out of his bag. He hit his stockings against the edge of the sledge that stuck out from a snowbank. "These socks look like two thin boards," he said through chattering teeth. "Our dressing room is the inland ice."

He shook the snow out of his trousers and

stepped into them. "Think how good some hot tea will taste as soon as we can dig out the food. *B-r-r-r-r*. The inside of this fur coat is colder than an icebox."

Peary sat down to pull on his frozen boots. He had to thaw them inch by inch by the warmth of his feet. "This storm has taught me two things," he said thoughtfully. He wriggled his feet farther and farther into his boots.

"I can guess one of them," Astrup said. "We should always sleep with our clothing *inside* our sleeping bags."

Peary nodded. "And the other one is not to build ice houses with flat walls. After this we'll put up igloos as the Eskimos do. Those round houses are so strong even an Arctic storm can't batter them down. The wind slips around them."

The men had to return to home base and wait for better weather before they could start out again. The second time Peary set out with four members of his party. This journey began no more easily than the first. There were delays. More food was used than they could spare.

Peary decided he could make better time with only one companion. All four men wanted to go on with him, but he chose Eivind Astrup.

With sixteen dogs to pull the sledges the two men traveled clear across the northern end of the icebound continent. Peary then proved his idea that Greenland was an island. This journey to the northeast coast and back was 1,300 miles long. The trip to the northeast coast ended on the Fourth of July.

The great explorer stood on the top of a towering cliff. He gazed at the bay far below. "In honor of this day," he said, "I name it Independence Bay. And this cliff I name Navy Cliff."

"Lieutenant Peary," Astrup said, "you have just finished an exploit that will make every

American proud of you!" His eyes glowed with admiration as he looked at his leader.

Robert Peary nodded without really hearing. He was staring to the north. He said, "No explorer has ever been as far north as you and I are standing right now, Astrup. But there's farther still to go. There is the North Pole! And, with God's help, I will reach the Pole some day."

"Do you think there is any way?" Astrup began doubtfully.

Peary said, "Where there's a will, there's a way."

From that moment, he was dedicated to one idea: to travel to the point of "Farthest North."

XIV

THE NORTH POLE!

1. *A Great Leader*

ROBERT PEARY spent the next sixteen years trying to reach the North Pole. For some of
his expeditions he had a hard time getting leave
from his Navy duties. Nearly always he was in
need of money to pay for his long journeys. Spe-
cially built ships were needed to break the ice,
and much special equipment for land travel.

After his discovery of Independence Bay he
was hailed in the United States as a hero. But
when his attempts to penetrate all the way to the
North Pole ended in failure, the public turned
against him.

"Why throw money away?" newspaper writ-
ers grumbled. "Why endanger lives in this fool-

ish attempt to reach a spot that *cannot* be reached? Commander Peary is a madman!"

One person never lost faith in him. That was his wife Josephine. Several times she went north with him. She would live for months in a camp on the west coast of Greenland while Robert and his men made their long and dangerous ventures toward the Pole.

The men who traveled with Peary were always enthusiastic in praising him. On the expedition in 1905 a group of his men sat talking.

"He's a great leader," said Mr. Clark, one of Peary's assistants. "He never asks a man to do a thing he wouldn't do himself."

"He's always thinking about the health and safety of his crew," said Dr. Wolf, the expedition's surgeon.

"And he's absolutely fair," Matt Henson agreed. "I've worked with him ever since he was sent to Nicaragua. I know he won't let any injustice be done."

"I'd follow him anywhere," declared Mr. Marvin, Peary's other assistant.

"Did you ever see a man with such courage?" Captain Bob Bartlett asked. He was skipper of Peary's new ship, the *Roosevelt*. "I was first mate on the *Windward* on the last expedition. I say Peary isn't afraid of anything!"

"No, and when he fails he just tries and tries again," Matt Henson said.

"Pearyokshwa—he never gives up," said one of Peary's Eskimo friends.

"He's not just an adventurer," Captain Bartlett said. "His Arctic trips have added a great deal to the world's knowledge. Peary has learned much about Arctic weather. He's learned about the flow of ice and about the mineral riches of this northern country."

Dr. Wolf added, "Peary's maps and his weather observations and all his scientific notes are carefully made. They're completely accurate."

"Do you know," asked Captain Bartlett, "that Peary froze both his feet on the last expedition? He never talks about it. He suffered terrible pain. For weeks he lay on his back in a dreary camp. We know what it's like during the Arctic night, when the sun doesn't rise for months. He had nothing to look back on but hardship and failure, and that terrible pain gripped him."

"Yes, but he was not dismayed—not Peary," Matt Henson said quickly. "It was during that bad time, when he couldn't get out of bed, that he wrote his motto on the cabin wall."

"What motto?" Clark asked.

"Why, the motto he has followed ever since he was a schoolboy. I saw it myself. It goes: 'I shall find a way, or make one!'"

2. *Dash to the Pole*

Robert Peary refused to be defeated. He was determined to reach the North Pole. He tried and failed, and he tried and failed. Then he tried once again.

"I always expect delays in the North," he told Captain Bob Bartlett, again the skipper of the *Roosevelt*. "We have to wait through the long months of darkness before we can make our dash for the Pole. Sometimes we have to wait for open water lanes to freeze before we can get our sledges over them. But at least we're on our way to the Pole then. It's this waiting in New York that makes me so impatient!"

Peary's savings were far from enough. Members of the Peary Arctic Club helped a great deal. But not until individuals gave still more money could the expedition start. Well stocked with supplies, the *Roosevelt* steamed out of New York harbor in July 1908.

In September the ship reached the farthest point it could go. During the dark months Peary organized hunting and scouting parties and saw that the equipment was in good shape.

In February the days began to grow light. Then Peary struck out across the ice with six white men, nineteen Eskimos and one hundred forty-six dogs. Snow was falling and the roaring wind whipped it against their faces and covered supplies on the sledges. Days of blizzards and numbing cold followed one another.

They plodded on till they came to a wide channel of swirling water. "We can't go around that," Peary said. "There must be some way to get across."

Bartlett laughed. "You said you expect delays in the North. But you'll do your best to overcome them in the shortest time possible."

The *Roosevelt* reached the farthest point it could go.

"From the looks of this water we're in for a long delay this time," Peary said.

They made camp beside the water. On the second day Bartlett ran to the base. "One of the Eskimos has found a bridge of ice. This may be the answer."

With the dogs and sledges all the men followed the Eskimo to the bridge. They worked their way cautiously part way across the channel. Peary, at the front of the line, stopped suddenly. "Back!" he shouted. "Turn back! From here to shore there's nothing underfoot but slush!"

The men retreated hastily across the narrow ice bridge. They camped five more dismal days beside the water.

Peary was breaking up a sledge for firewood when an Eskimo dashed into camp. "Pearyokshwa, young ice forms there!" He pointed far beyond the camp.

That was all Peary was waiting to hear.

Quickly he gave orders to load the sledges. He started across the ice, walking with his feet far apart. It was like rubber, swaying with every step he took. He raised his hand to signal the others. One by one the men moved cautiously across the new ice.

At last all of them had crossed safely. Then Bartlett shouted, "Look! The ice is parting!" As they watched, the thin ice broke apart. Swirling icy water rushed freely down the channel again.

For two days the men dragged themselves through a muddle of shattered ice. Some fragments were as big as paving stones. Others were many times larger than that. All the men staggered from weakness.

Finally Peary stopped. "We'll camp here," he said.

The weary men slumped to the ground. They were glad to stop and rest. But Peary remained on his feet. He lifted his telescope and swept it around the horizon for a last look before he sat down.

"What's that!" he exclaimed sharply. "Something's moving about five or six miles away. . . . I can see what it is now. Two . . . four . . . six . . . seven musk oxen!"

"Musk oxen! Are you sure?" Bartlett cried.

"It seems too good to be true," Peary said. "But there they are!"

He reached for his rifle. "Come on," he said to one of the Eskimos. "We'll hunt them down."

He and the Eskimo set out on snowshoes toward the little herd of oxen. When they came within range of the animals, Peary lifted his rifle. He lowered it immediately. He was so weak he had to rest, catch his breath and wait till he could control the trembling in his arms. Then he lifted the gun again. This time his aim was steady. One by one all seven oxen fell.

The rest of the party moved their camp to the ground where the animals lay. "Now for a handsome feast!" Peary said. They cooked the meat and regained their strength while they rested.

Peary knew from his earlier journeys that only a small party could travel fast in the last part of the dash to the Pole. Along the way he sent members of the expedition back to the ship in small groups. Some of them had gone ahead to break trail. They were near exhaustion.

Captain Bartlett was the last of Peary's crew to turn back. Then Peary had five men in his party —Matt Henson and four Eskimos.

On April 6, 1909, exactly nine months after Peary had left New York, he took readings on his instruments and said, "We're three miles from the North Pole."

"Hurry!" an Eskimo exclaimed.

"Not now," Peary said. Weariness lined his

Peary thrust the flagpole into the ice.

weather-beaten face. "I'm eager to reach the Pole too. But we've traveled hard for many hours without stopping. Now we'll rest a few hours."

They stopped for a short time and then went on over the three miles between them and the Pole. The Eskimo who had wanted to hurry looked all about him. There was solid ice as far as he could see. "North Pole, you say. Where Big Nail?"

Peary's brow wrinkled. "What big nail?"

"I saw round world on ship. Big Nail sticks out end."

Peary laughed. "You're talking about the globe—the rod that sticks out the end so the globe will spin around! No, there's no big nail at the North Pole. But there'll be a long pole sticking here in just a minute."

He reached into a canvas bag and took out an

American flag. He attached it to a pole and thrust it firmly into the ice. The five men standing around him cheered. Peary shook hands with them and beamed.

He had tried again and this time he had won!

8527